I AIN'T 'AVING THAT

a novel for our times

BY

MARTIN ROGERS

Illustrations by Lee R Healey

An *I Ain't 'Aving That*® production

Published by Vectra Publications
Typeset and designed by Eyelevel Books
Printed in England by
Biddles Limited

First published in the United Kingdom by Vectra Publications

ISBN: 1-902528-12-3

Visit us today at: www.iaintavingthat.com
or e-mail: martinrogers@iaintavingthat.com

This book is dedicated to Danielle, Michelle, Nicole, Richard, Sarah, Terry and Tracy, with love and affection

Special thanks to Roger St. Pierre for helping me put my thoughts into words, and to Andrew and Phillip for all their help and encouragement.

Based on real people in real situations, this is a book about life as it is. It's as much about you as it is about me. Welcome to my world.

CONTENTS

FOOTNOTES

FOREWORD

Part novel, part autobiography, part social commentary, part survival guide *"I Ain't 'Aving That"* is all those things and more. Most of all it's a laugh a line account of one man's struggle against the system which so blights all our daily lives.

Bar room philosopher, barrack room lawyer and sworn enemy of every police officer, parking warden, council official or shop manager who ever tried to throw his or her weight around, Martin Rogers has a unique take on getting by.

At the urging of friends and family who have so often split their sides with laughing at his antics, Martin decided to turn a pen usually reserved for writing letters of complaint, petitions and writs to authoring this book.

You'll find that many of the things that happen to Martin have also happened to you, your family or friends at some time or other. It's just that they happen more often and in greater diversity to a man who describes himself without blushing as "a walking disaster, a serial fuck-up" but who, in fact, is set to become the common man's hero. For Martin never fails to fight back against everything that's thrown at him. In short, he ain't 'aving that.

Laced with the street lore and humour of South London, *"I Ain't 'Aving That"* will bring a constant smile to every reader's lips...

Martin Rogers is definitely not one of life's winners. In fact, he seems to stumble from one crisis to another. But he isn't a loser either – for here's someone who simply won't stand for the shit the world so regularly throws at him.

His attitude to life's trials and tribulations is simple: "I ain't 'aving that!"

Two failed marriages, a succession of jobs and frequent changes of address punctuate a life which sees him constantly running up against the system – but there's no way the buggers are going to grind him down.

He'll battle them with a flood of phone calls and sarcastic letters; he'll fight them through the courts and he'll even resort to chaining himself to the railings if needs be.

"*I Ain't 'Aving That*" is an hilarious account of one man's refusal to be a victim and determination to fight for his rights. It stands as a shining example to everyone who has ever waited in all morning for a gas man who never showed up; who's ever run foul of a stroppy traffic warden or who's tried to fight the council through the courts.

He has run-ins with shop assistants and builders, with policemen and taxi drivers. Though he doesn't always come out on top, they all regret the day they took him on.

There's a little bit of Martin Rogers in all of us. Bad luck happens to everyone (especially our hero) but his indomitable spirit proves you can make your own good luck. True, Martin is a cert for slipping on that banana skin – but you can bet your boots he'll find someone to sue for his resultant broken arm.

A novel for our times, "*I Ain't 'Aving That*" isn't a comedy but it is extremely funny, laced with the humour to be found in everyday situations; it isn't a textbook but it's filled with object lessons for us all.

Read, learn, but above all, enjoy...

Roger St. Pierre, London August 2001

I AIN'T 'AVING THAT

a novel for our times

BEGINNINGS

London Cockneys reckon it's good luck to accidentally step in dog shit. I think it must be on the basis that nothing much worse can happen; so, after that, life must inevitably take an upturn.

My trouble, though, is that as soon as I scrape the crap off my size eights I go and step in some more of it. I'm the kind of geezer who walks around a ladder to avoid the bad luck of walking under it, only for the painter to take a tumble and fall down on me, paint pot and all. Me, I'm a serial fuck-up, a right magnet for grief.

Mind you, while I am often so deep in the mire that it's threatening to clog up my left nostril, I always somehow manage to squeeze my way out of the ultimate conclusion of my impending disasters. I remember facing eviction once. I was clearing my gear out and tucked in the back of a drawer I found a crumpled wad of tenners – not enough to solve my problems, you understand, but sufficient to turn the bailiffs from the door and buy me some time.

Four kids, two wives, two divorces – it's the kind of scoreline you'd expect from Crystal Palace on a bad Saturday. That's me, Martin Rogers. 30 something, still dreaming, still scheming, ducking and diving my way through life's problems and religiously following that old motto about not letting the buggers grind you down.

"I ain't 'aving that": That's my motto in life. I hate it when I know someone is lying to me, trying to give me the right run around, stringing me along, out to rip me off or just giving me a load of crap. I think to myself: "I know I'm right but they are trying to tell me I'm wrong – and I ain't 'aving that".

"Don't mess with me!" – that's my message, because I come with a government health warning.

It's amazing the amount of people who get themselves stitched up like a kipper, meekly accepting the first and usually negative answer in response to a complaint, or who just get intimidated by a shopkeeper or someone at customer services in Marks and Sparks. Well mate, I'm not that type of person, as you will quickly learn…

I honestly feel that I have a big black cloud hovering directly above my head and that I'm doomed to suffer bad luck all along life's bumpy highway. If it's going to happen to anyone, be sure it will happen to me – with a vengeance that verges on the downright malicious. They say that bad luck comes in threes; well, in my case it comes neatly packaged by the dozen. I wonder if breaking a mirror really does mean seven years' bad luck? – if so, I've got another two years still to do!

But what makes me different from most of the berks out there is that I don't accept all the garbage that's thrown at me – I fight back and often turn things on their head and come out as some kind of winner, or at least with the satisfaction that I've made life as difficult for my adversaries – a Woolworth's broken biscuits-style assortment of coppers, parking wardens, council officials, shop managers and plain and simple wankers – as they have made it for me.

They say every cloud has a silver lining and while nobody likes being cheated or bashed around, if, at the end of the day, you drag the people against you through the courts and show them up for the tossers they are and perhaps even come out with a compensation award of a couple of grand, maybe all the aggravation is worthwhile. Whatever, it certainly makes life's experience richer!

There's simply no reason to lay down and meekly accept what life – and all its toss-pots – throws at you. When things are bang out of order, you've got to fight back, haven't you? Am I right or am I right?

You can't go through life letting people take advantage of you, just because you're too embarrassed or too shy to speak out or are scared shitless of losing. I don't give a fiddlers if people think I'm a stroppy dickhead. If I know I'm right then I stick to my guns like Wyatt Earpe and won't take "no" for an answer. At the very least, I make sure I give the bastards a right hard time. If you, on the other hand, choose not to do anything about it, you can't really moan – you'll end up the loser; the one out of pocket and boring all your mates by whinging on and on about it. Face it: life isn't designed to be fair. It's up to each of us to defend our own corner and if, along the way, we can help others do the same, then so much the better.

That's the reason I decided to document my life. Honest guv, when I sat down with me Bic and started scribbling these notes it was not some ego trip or a conspiracy to denude the earth of its rain forests – well, to be honest, there was an element of spotlight-seeking; hopefully it'll make me mum feel all proud and might even impress that barmaid with the big knockers at The East Dulwich Tavern. No, my real motivation for burning all this midnight oil and getting my story down on paper has been so I can pass my experiences on and maybe help you lot out there to sort your problems out with the minimum expense and aggravation. And, let's face it, as I have already pointed out, you do have to fight your own battles.

In my own experience I have found that the process of sorting things for myself has been much more effective and a lot quicker than relying on others to do it for me. However helpful the people at Citizen's Advice might be, you're not their first priority. No, half their mind will always be on their own problems – one of which is to get shot of you as painlessly as possible – and the other will be fixated on what's going to 'appen on "East Enders" tonight.

The good Lord really does help he who helps himself – though the Devil will be right there to kick the feet from under you at every chance he gets. As my ol' mum, Irene, is fond of saying: "Don't ask, don't want" (though I have to admit she usually adds "Ask, don't get!").

I'm sick to death of seeing my friends and acquaintances being taken advantage of. I've been there, seen it, done it (but couldn't afford the T-shirt!) so I decided to pass my experiences on for the benefit of others.

Life is like a shit sandwich. The more bread you've got the less shit you have to eat. Money might not make you happy, but it's a good down payment on an easier life and rich people generally get by with less aggravation than hits us ordinary folks. But even if you are skint, in a crap job, even on the dole, you don't have to walk along with two feet in the gutter feeling sorry for yourself and doing nothing in response to being generally ripped off, pissed on and messed about.

It might be small consolation as you sit there contemplating your Giro but even the wealthy often make the mistake of blindly accepting whatever line they are told and letting people trample all over them.

One of the customers on our milk round when I was a kid helping our old Ron on his deliveries of gold top was a retired RAF wing commander who had returned to civvy street and made a small fortune in the supermarket business before parking his trolley for the last time and devoting himself to mowing the lawn and writing letters to The Times as "Angry, of Dulwich".

As a hangover from his working days, he was running a £20,000 overdraft on his current account at the local bank, banging up interest and charges, but had £60,000 sitting on deposit at the very same branch, earning miserably low interest. It meant that, effectively, he was paying – and through the nose, at that – to borrow his own money!

But when he asked the bank manager to switch money between the two accounts he was told he couldn't do that as the funds in his deposit account had been frozen as security for his overdraft!

Bruce was a friendly old geezer who always asked us in for a cuppa and one morning, as we nibbled on his chocolate digestives, he was moaning to Ron and me about all this – and how it had been going on for some months. I was just a snot-nosed little kid with his shirt tail hanging out, but even at my tender age I could suss that the old boy was being ripped off in a right old fashion, so I told him he should go to see the local solicitor. And, yes, it took just one strongly worded letter from the legal eagle to get the wanker, sorry, banker, to back down and refund all that interest and the bank charges too.

Not that the old boy had any reason to trust solicitors any more than the bank. Sometime earlier his maiden aunt had popped her clogs. One day there was a knock at his door and there stood a smooth looking gent all suited and booted in an immaculate pin-stripe, with shoes shone so you could see the reflection of your face in them, and carrying an important looking black leather document case.

He revealed that the aunt had left a will stating that her not inconsiderable estate should be divided up among all her "surviving known relatives". It seemed the solicitors, appointed by her as executors of her estate, had been travelling the world – first-class, of course – burning their way through her fortune, trying to track down her family. Expensive hotels – with room service, of course – air tickets, luxury hire-cars: all, they argued, necessary to enable them to carry out their appointed task, were all methodically charged to the estate. They didn't give a monkeys that it was someone else's wedge they were slicing into.

So it was that the unexpected caller was doorstepping not to bring the news of good fortune but to blithely announce that he was looking for a contribution from our friend, and all the other traced members of the far-flung family. He said this was to cover the balance of what had turned from a fortune into a short-fall of funds, and could he have the money now please? – certified cheque preferred, the cheeky bastard.

Truth is, lawyers are there to make money for lawyers. Get them involved in a dispute which could be settled by just sitting down with the other side and talking about it sensibly over a couple of beers and it turns into a near war

which costs both sides a fortune. That's never more so than
when it's a divorce that's involved.

But this doesn't mean that you should ignore the
importance of the law as a potent weapon in your battles
against the system. I'm an easy-going sort but make no
mistake, I can be right in yer face when I get a strop on. As
you'll soon learn, I'm no slouch when it comes to slapping
a writ on someone who is trying to duff me up one way or
another.

The secret is to become a bit of a barrack-room lawyer,
do plenty of homework so you know exactly where you
stand and carry out as much of the legal process for
yourself as you can before wheeling out some expensive
brief to finish the job with a low punch to the solar plexus.

You have to learn on your feet, recognising the scams
that can work in your favour and the ones which will be
used against you. I'm sure that somewhere in these pages
there will be a situation that you can relate to. It might help
you to know how I dealt with the problem – or, at least,
tried to deal, with it – and, at worst, you can have a few
laughs at my expense.

I come from a bona fide South London clan. I don't
know if we were Saxons already squatting on the wrong
side of London Bridge when the Normans arrived or if my
ancestors were Frogs, camp-following old William The
Conqueror – or Guillaume Le Batard, as the French called
him, and I bet he was a right bastard too! – but there's been
untold generations of us in these parts. Born in Guy's
Hospital, my first home was a grotty council flat in
Bermondsey.

I'm a South Londoner through to the bone. We know
our roots in this manor. And they are dug deep. We sit
down here on our verandahs, watching the great red blob
of the sun sink slowly behind the palm trees and
cottonfields while we think of those poor northern gits in
Hampstead and Hendon, up above the snow line, freezing
their knackers off.

Britain's biggest north/south divide is not that between
those beyond the Watford Gap and those in the Smoke but

the one that separates the people settled on either side of the snaking River Thames. To each his own, and each regards the other's territory as being a bland, dirty, characterless mass of lookalike urban sprawl.

Invite someone from my neck of the woods for a night out in Brighton – 50 miles away – and they'll jump at the idea. Suggest instead a trip across the river to Highgate, which you can actually see from the top of my road and get to by red bus too, with only one change, and they'd cringe at the very idea: "No, it's too far away, mate. Can't be arsed dragging all the way up there."

It's a Berlin Wall style divide, though of a psychological rather than physical nature. Reinforced by such considerations as black cab drivers' positive aversion to carrying fares south, it exerts an extraordinarily important role in people's decision as to where to live. But it's not as if you have to breach Check Point Charlie to cross it.

We meet on neutral ground in the City and West End to earn our daily bread but in essence North and South Londoners are two totally different breeds. This, then, is essentially a story about life in South London. That said, it contains lessons which have a relevance wherever in London, or that matter, wherever in the world you happen to park your backside.

With the demise of the docks and the moving out of the old, close-knit community to all those shitty new towns, Bermondsey changed – and not for the better. It was time to move on and after the old man did a nifty council flat swap, I grew up – or was dragged up, I should say – from the age of seven or so on a rough-and-ready council estate just off Dog Kennel Hill in South London's East Dulwich suburb, half-a-mile and several hundred thousand pounds from leafy Dulwich Village.

I have to say, most of the dogs lived in those flats rather than in kennels. Shit, were some of those mingers ugly or what? It didn't stop us from offering them a slice of our pocket money to show us their drawers though.

Mum and dad knocked four of us kids out before they realised what was causing the problem. Then they started watching telly instead. My oldest brother flew the nest before I was out of primary school, so I was always closest to my younger brother, Luke – or Nobby as he's known to his mates – and to my sis, Faye, who is a year older than me.

Luke's a lazy basket. They talk about people living life in the fast lane; well, he lives it on the hard shoulder. He's so laid-back sometimes, you have to take his pulse to make sure he's still alive. I love the geezer though, 'cos he's my bruv.

Faye's great. Not only does she like the same music and think on the same wavelength as me but she's always had dozens of friends, providing me with a rich and happy hunting ground for hot totty. She's also always been good for a sub if I run short of readies before my next deal comes through.

On top of that we had enough cousins, most of 'em right toe-rags, to form a pretty formidable platoon in the British Army – that is if they could ever be rounded up and didn't all go awol.

Then there were all my uncles and aunts, dotted all over the smoke, from Dagenham to Hammersmith, and especially down in South, no, make that 'Sarf' London – the land of sunshine and plenty.

Now I don't want to sound like those old Yorkshire gits from that memorable *Monty Python* episode but sometimes we did 'ave it a bit tough. I wasn't exactly brought up in a shoe box but some of the council flats we had were pretty rough and ready, though we eventually got a decent four-bedroom terraced house and under Maggie Thatcher's 'right to buy' scheme, mum and dad were able to saddle themselves with a mortgage, courtesy of the Woolwich.

As a small kid I took a few bashings from the other lads on the block – and from my big brother and my sister too – and I wasn't exactly flush with pocket money neither. I was taught from an early age to stick up for myself and was weaned on the very sensible attitude that if you want something then you have to get up off your arse and go out and get it for yourself.

As me old mum used to say: "If you can't fight your own battles you can't expect anyone else to fight them for you", though she did also hammer home the message: "If I catch you fighting, you little bleeder, I'll give you what for – and I won't wait for your father to get 'ome neither."

The simple truth is, nothing in this life is going to fall into your lap without at least a little arm-twisting and pushing on your part and I'm eternally grateful to my mum and dad for drumming that simple fact into me.

It served me well in my school, which was a right rough-house comprehensive, with teachers who weren't backwards in coming forwards when it came to corporal punishment. It was one of the last state schools to still wallop kids and I was, naturally, a regular for the cane – which, in any case, I far preferred to detention. It was short, sharp and soon forgotten, whereas, if you were kept in after school you lost a couple of hours of your precious free time and then got a right larraping anyway when the old man twigged on to why you were late home.

I was an expert at taking the medicine. Old Solly, the perverted little maths teacher who liked nothing better than twisting ears and pinching necks, would send me to the headmaster's study to fetch the cane. 'Adolph', as we knew the head, kept those vicious little bamboo twigs in a big, tall pot just inside the door. I'd pick out the very thickest one I could find, 'cause it's the thin, swishy ones that hurt most. Then I'd hurry back to the classroom, stopping in the bogs on the way to rub some soap into my palms, which takes away the sting.

I soon learnt not to pull my hand out of the sweeping arc of Solly's sadistic punishment because if the cane caught the top of your fingers rather than the flat of the hand then that was just about as excruciating as getting your dick caught in your zipper.

Solly was a sarcastic old bleeder too. We had this posh kid come to the school, He'd been kicked out of Dulwich College, the local toffee-nose public school where not only PG Woodehouse and Raymond Chandler were once pupils – imagine that, Jeeves and Wooster and Philip Marlowe all being products of the same school! – but so too, I've heard it rumoured, was Hitler's deputy, Martin Boorman, though the school keeps quiet about that little fact.

Calling the register, Old Solly would take delight in pronouncing that kid's name as "Smith", which always drew the exasperated response: "It's not Smith Sir, it's Smyth," until one day Solly exploded: "Smith, Smythe, shit, shyte – it's all the same to me!"

Solly the sadist eventually got his comeuppance when a group of fifth formers broke into the school the night before the end of term when they were due to be thrown out into the big wide world. Not only did they take all the desks and chairs out of the school and arrange them in neat lines on the playground but they somehow managed to get Solly's beaten up old Morris Minor Traveller up onto a flat roof and a crane had to be brought in to get it back down.

Painting "Gestapo Headquarters" across the school roof in two-feet high letters didn't endear those kids to the school authorities either but nobody ever found out who was responsible and even if we'd known, none of us, not even, I suspect, snooty Smythe, would have grassed 'em up.

Dosh was always tight at home, so I couldn't rely, like so many of today's kids, on a constant supply of pocket money. Consequently, I developed into a bit of a wheeler dealer at school. For instance, I had a good little line in flogging school dinner tickets on the cheap. Most of the kids from poor homes who got these hand-outs actually preferred bunking off out of school during lunch break, so they could have a crafty ciggie and nip into the local chippie to feed their acne on some greasy chips.

I realised that there was money to be made from buying up their unused dinner tickets and selling them on at a discounted price to the posher kids who had to pay full whack for their school dinners. By buying the tickets off me, these kids could use what was left over from the money their mums had given them for school dinner in order to buy sweets, fags, porno mags or whatever else they weren't supposed to have. I made a nice little packet this way and it didn't stop there.

It was in the days when the telephone boxes were all painted red and were still taking the old pre-decimalisation twopenny and tenpence pieces. I'd fill my pockets with penny coins and go up to soft-touch looking people on busy shopping streets and ask them if they could give me a twopence for the phone. Most of them would give me the coin I was after but didn't bother to take the two pennies I offered in exchange. They simply walked off, pre-occupied with what piece of scrag-end they were going to buy the old man for his tea.

As the hours slipped by, I became progressively richer and it was costing me no money and precious little effort to make my fortune. I know we are just talking coppers here but it was like a goldmine to a snot-nosed little 12-year old. They do say "Take care of the pennies and the pounds will take care of themselves" – and they're dead right. After all, that's the way FW Woolworth made his fortune. What's more, once I had totted up enough money to buy a 10 pack of cheapo cigarettes – something called Number 6, I seem to remember – I would take 'em back to school and sell the fags as singles at a massive mark-up, making even more cash for myself.

At weekends I'd be up really early to do my paper round, then I'd help Ron, the milkman, on his deliveries. Saturdays and Sundays were his busiest days as that was when he would have to doorstep, rattling all the knockers and asking his customers to settle their milk bills for the week. Lots of people didn't have a clue about how much they actually owed as they'd run their tally up for weeks at a time. Ron would tell me how much to ask for and, if I thought I'd get away with it, I'd add a few bob on – not a lot but enough to give me a little bit of extra pocket money in case I ever managed to work out what the barber meant when he asked: "Need anything for the weekend Sir?"

I usually ended up with a fair bit of change jangling in my pocket – and I didn't 'alf hate the people who unknowingly fouled me by always paying by cheque! Somehow it didn't seem to me like stealing, it was just a sort of involuntary tipping system for turning out on all those dark, damp, brass monkey mornings and making sure everyone had some fresh milk to pour over their Ready-Brek while I was working out how to defrost my fingers.

My mum wasn't too much of a cook. She grew up in that school of British culinary art which believed that cabbage wasn't done until the whole street reeked of it. Her brussels sprouts turned out as so much mush. Question: "What's the difference between bogies and brussels sprouts?" Answer: "you can't get your kids to eat their brussels sprouts!"

She did, though, make brilliant bread pudding. Heavyweight stuff, it weighed in like a battleship – making it wonderful for hand-to-hand fighting. In fact, it was rumoured that the Yanks were getting worried about its potency and were suggesting a 'Bread Pudding Non-proliferation Pact'!

Now there was no way I was going to lug the stuff round with me but people on the milk round got to hear about how tasty it was, so Mum would make a couple of extra trays. I'd take orders without Ron ever twigging what was going on and one of my uncles who was out of work and who split the take with me would drop off the orders later and collect the pennies. We didn't coin a lot but it kept him in fags for a day or two and I was up for anything I could make.

I'd developed a good line in cheeky patter, so the housewives took a shine to me and I used to pick up a pocketful of tips to add to what Ron paid me and what I skimmed off the top (not of the milk, but with my little scams!). I had some other nice little earners going too – washing people's cars, gardening, doing shopping errands for people too busy, too old or too lazy to do it for themselves – so really I did alright for myself. I remember clearly that from a very early age I was determined that I would be a millionaire by the time I was 30. Truth was, I got off to a very promising start. Needless to say it was all downhill from then on and the words 'negative equity' are now firmly entrenched in my vocabulary.

Not hitting the big time hasn't been for lack of ideas and effort, of course. I've pulled a million strokes and have never let any opportunity slip me by. For instance, I remember when the dustmen used to go out on strike. I'd walk round our estate with a wheelbarrow and charge 20 pence a bag to take the rubbish away, dropping that to 10 pence for the elderly. Most of the people on the estate were well up for it as the smell from the garbage piling up was dreadful. Northerners are always telling us that "Where there's muck, there's brass" – and ain't that the truth!

There was a great big house, a right mansion really, stranded on a convenient nearby housing estate, and it was due to be pulled down to make way for a new comprehensive school. On the Sunday before the day set to be its date with the demolition man's wrecking ball, this once proud stately pile stood empty, lonely and forlorn. I nipped round sharpish, found an old barrow in a tumbledown shed in the garden and loaded it up with as many shrubs as I could manage to dig up before anyone turned up to ask what I thought I was doing of. I then did a door-knocking round of the estate, flogging the plants off as fast as I could before anyone cottoned on to where they were coming from.

After I'd sold the lot and stripped all the doors of brass handles and flogged them too, along with anything else that wasn't firmly nailed down, I then sold the wheelbarrow, by which time it was getting dark. I was in no rush to get home to watch "Songs Of Praise" so I slipped back to the shed for a crafty fag. Unfortunately, as my mum reminded me ruefully just the other day, I inadvertently managed to burn the shed down, having left an oil lamp alight on the floor.

Even when the snow fell and all the other kids were indoors huddled round the electric fire eating Bovril on toast, I was out there earning a few bob, clearing pathways with my shovel and salt. And when I wasn't shovelling snow I was shovelling shit at the riding stables in Dulwich Park, taking the stuff home, still steaming, in a plastic bag for me mum to put on her strawberries (posh people had cream!).

When I wasn't needed on Ron's milk round, I had a nice little scam going at the pictures. On Saturday mornings, we'd go to the local fleapit in Camberwell – it's been ripped down now, of course, and replaced with an office block – and once the lights went down I'd nip to the emergency exit and let my mates slip in without paying. Then, when it was all over and people were trooping out, I'd look under the seats and usually find enough dropped change – even sometimes a fiver or a tenner note – so my next week's admission and the cost of a choc ice were already taken care of. Truth is, I might not have been learning much at school but I was doing all right for myself out on the streets, truancy officers notwithstanding.

AND THEN
THE GRIEF BEGAN

Life wasn't all a breeze though. Authority was already raising its ugly head and there seemed to be a queue of people waiting in line to take a pop at me. If it wasn't Mrs Brown at number 42 complaining to Ron that I didn't leave her any gold top yesterday, which I bleeding well did, it was that shit English teacher caning me because I couldn't spell 'hooligan', which he insisted should have been my middle name.

I left school when I was 15, a year younger than was the normal leaving age. No, let's be honest, I didn't leave in the normal sense, I was politely told to piss off – if not in those exact words. I called it "Time off for bad behaviour".

I had no school certificates – I hadn't even sat any exams – and no qualifications for the big wide world, except what I'd taught myself already out on the streets in the university of life.

It didn't take me long to cotton on to drawing benefit and I really looked forward to my fortnightly Giro cheque dropping on the door-mat. It seemed a great club to join – and no membership fee to pay neither.

But there was Pop, going on and on and on like a Des O'Connor record, telling me I should get off my arse and get a job and threatening to kick me out, so I bowed to the inevitable and trudged down to the local job centre.

The first pay-packet of my life came from a firm of quantity surveyors and building costs consultants. That sounds grand but all I was was a glorified gofer – "Go fer this, go fer that!"

I'd be hurtling all over the West End, risking life and limb and running myself ragged for real crap money – and forever getting stopped by the police 'cause they reckoned I looked too young to be riding anything more than a Raleigh Chopper, not that my mankey 50cc Honda moped posed any danger to other road users.

No, the biggest risk was the potential damage to my pride and my reputation as a 'face' if any of me mates should spot me riding that scabby pop-pop. I could just imagine them having a great time taking the piss out of me and my mobile hairdryer.

After a few weeks, the firm got me a little secondhand motorbike and I felt a bit better, though, as a latter-day mod, I would have been a lot happier with a Lambretta or a Vespa. Inevitably, I eventually got nicked. The cozzer who gave me a tug reckoned the seat was dangerously loose and the shock absorbers dodgy too. But the bike was owned and meticulously maintained by the company and had sailed through its MOT test only the week before.

It took four months for the case to come up, so I had plenty of time to get down to the library and bone up on the law. As you'll have guessed, I'd decided "I ain't 'aving that" and was determined to fight the bastards all the way. I represented myself in court, said "Yes Sir, please Sir, three bags full Sir," in all the right places, and not only was the case thrown out but I was awarded 80 quid costs from the police for my inconvenience.

It was my first time chalking one up against the system, and boy did it feel good. Of course, it helped that the chairwoman of the bench was an old biddy who took a shine to me as I stood there all neatly ironed and pressed, with hair cut to regulation length and not a strand out of place. I put on me posh voice too – the one my kids always accuse me of using whenever I am on the blower.

The Old Bill got their own back on me some months later when I was caught bang to rights riding without L-plates.

What happened was I'd just bought a secondhand Lambretta scooter from an ad in the Exchange & Mart. As I've said, I fancied myself as a bit of a second-generation mod at the time. I felt I was the bee's knees, the mutt's nuts, on that bleeding death trap, with its skinny arse little wheels and a unfortunate tendency to topple over on wet and greasy corners, leaving as big a skid mark in me boxers as on the road.

Anyway, I for some reason assumed the scooter would have L-plates already on it – after all, most people have already moved on to a car before they get round to taking a two-wheeler test.

I was going to a football club dinner and dance that night and was already all togged up in my best whistle and flute, a dab of Brut behind each lug 'ole and one on me belly button for good measure, so off I tootled feeling like a right Jack the Lad. It was just before Christmas and bleeding cold enough to freeze the balls off the proverbial brass monkey.

There were lots of tasty sorts there, and one lovely blonde, with long, slim legs all the way up to her arse, kept eyeing me, but for some odd reason that might have had something to do with her catching me with one finger poking slyly up me nose mining for coal, I didn't manage to pull.

I felt I had to show off to someone, though, so I offered one of my muckas a lift home. That was a long drag from my manor, somewhere over Bromley way, and by now it was well after midnight and getting colder by the second.

When we got there, Tom's old man made me a coffee and gave me a tot from his bottle of duty-free five-star Cognac, which normally only sees the light of day at weddings and funerals.

I have to admit it went to my head a tad – after all, being sweet 16, I was under-age for drinking at the time. On the way home I was wobbling a bit from the combined effects of the now sub-zero temperature and the brandy. I thought I was home and dry and was just turning into the estate when "nee nah, nee nah" – the Old Bill gave me a tug.

Presumably, they put my wobbling down to my not yet being a qualified rider because the first thing PC Plod said to me was: "You haven't had this bike long, have you Sir?"

I told him I'd just bought it that night and thought for a second that I was going to blag my way out of the situation but then he asked for my driving licence and informed me he was going to report me for riding without L-plates. I suppose I was lucky he hadn't caught me earlier when Tom was on the back, which would have made matters a lot worst. I was lucky too that he didn't decide to breathalyse me because it would have gone from green to red to bright purple.

Anyhows, he said I'd be hearing from the court in due course but months and months went by and not a dicky bird. I really thought I'd got away with it when one bright sunny morning a summons plopped onto the door-mat. It was lucky that for once I'd dragged myself out of my pit with the dawn chorus and got to it before me dad did. If he'd known I'd been pulled by the boys in blue he would have gone ape-shit. For, much though he hated the filth, the silly old bugger believed in doing everything by the rules, sticking to the book, never putting a foot wrong. He even thought going overdrawn at the bank was a mortal sin.

I had to blag a morning off work for the court hearing. I knew the score: dress smart but in no way flashy, be polite, look contrite and think fast on your feet.

While I was waiting for my case to be called, I got chatting to a young lad sitting next to me. He was a greaser... slicked down black hair, black stay-pressed jeans which were so tight they looked painted on, black leather bomber jacket, you know the type, but he seemed a decent enough bloke to me and was certainly no yobbo.

He told me he'd been pulled for only having one L-plate on his Yamaha: "The one on the back had fallen off and I hadn't noticed," was his excuse.

It sounded totally believable to me. Stands to reason, dunnit, if you were going to deliberately run around without L-plates then you'd ditch both of them, now wouldn't you?

His case was called before mine and the whole thing was over inside five minutes. He came back out with all the colour drained from his face and looking for all the world as if the beak had donned the dreaded black cap and ordered him to be dragged off to the gallows – with "And may God have mercy on your soul" ringing in his lug 'oles.

"Cor, the bastards threw the book at me," he whined, "They gave me a right ol' bollocking, called me a menace to society, fined me £80 and endorsed my licence."

"Shit," I thought, "What the fuck are they going to do to me? Transport me to the colonies or something?"

Was I quaking in my boots when my turn came! Forget bricks, I was shitting three-bed semis. I stood there looking full of remorse, spoke in a low, respectful tone, pleaded guilty and waited for the worst.

"£10 fine and don't let us see you here again, young man," intoned the magistrate imperiously over the top of her bi-focals.

I couldn't believe it. I was the one who had got off light, I suppose you could call it a right result on my part, but I felt aggrieved about the injustice of it. So that's the tariff: £10 fine for no L plates, an extra £70 fine and an endorsement for wearing a leather jacket!

But, then, as Tony, a solicitor's clerk mate of mine who can't wait for the revolution, is fond of pointing out: "Fairness don't come into it, Mart. The law isn't about justice, it's simply a means of keeping us all in line and creating an ordered society on behalf of the establishment."

By and large, though, I had come through my early years with a clean nose, despite shinning up all those trees, bunking over walls, nicking that old geezer down the road's apple crop, playing knockdown ginger and moving on to shooting at pigeons with me air gun.

It was my spotty young cousin Mark – "The Clearasil Kid" as we called him for his acne-ridden face which resembled an 18-hole golf course – who used to catch all the flack rather than me. He was younger than the rest of our little crowd, couldn't run as fast, and, back in those days, was dim as a Toc H lamp, though he caught up with us as he got older and became more street-wise.

LEARNING
THE GROUND RULES

I was a right one for the birds as a kid. I might not have been much of a looker but I had a good line in patter and it didn't hurt that my street savvy meant I could always get favours done for them and theirs: "Your dad's car failed its MOT? Shame, but don't worry luv, I know someone who can get him a hooky ticket." And, of course, I always made sure there was a drink in it for me. Fair's fair – if I'm gonna take his daughter out for a ruby murray after the flicks on Saturday night then it's only right that the old geezer should pay his whack towards it.

My old cinema dodges were duly updated. They had a rule at the Cat's Whiskers pulling-palace in Streatham – I think it's called Caesar's now – that you could not get in unless you were wearing a jacket and tie, and neither of my two mates at the time had a tie they'd be seen dead in. But the management never seemed bothered about people taking their ties off once they were inside the gaff. So I would pay to get in, go to the bogs for a jimmy riddle and pass my neck-strangler back out through the window so someone else could wear it. Those cauliflower-eared thicko bouncers on the door never ever twigged that the same brightly spotted gravy-stained tie had gone past them twice; or more likely, they didn't give a shit – just as long as you had a tie on when you walked past them because that was where their responsibility for the rules ended.

At lots of clubs they gave you a printed pass-out so you

could come back in once you'd gone out to get a kebab, run your younger sister home, have a quickie knee-trembler up the alley with some bird whose name you didn't even know, or whatever. But other gaffs would use a stamp to mark the back of your hand.

It didn't take me long to come up with a duplicate stamp of my own so I could get myself and my mates in for nothing. I was even tempted to sell half-priced admissions to strangers but I had enough nouse to twig that the security bozzos, thick though they might be, would soon cotton on to that, rumble me, and I'd be in for a right kicking.

Of course, like so many of my generation, it wasn't long before I'd learned the rudiments of back-row fumbling the assorted Tracys, Dawns, Sharons and Stacys who crossed my path, quickly moving on to dipping my wick and all the other pleasures of the flesh.

I'd upgraded meself to an old Ford Anglia van, not much in the comfort stakes but with plenty of room to lay down and get on the job in the back. It was a right wreck, always breaking down, and carried a permanent sick note as well as an MOT.

I carved many a notch on the gear stick of that old banger, a number of my scores coming with a bird from Southend. We'd met at a club in the West End. Her name was Tina and she was Essex girl personified. Talk about dim. Her conversation was like the proverbial 'yes, no, interlude':

"Have you been on holiday yet?"

"Yes."

"Where did you go?"

"Spain."

"Did you have a nice time?"

"Yes."

"What was the weather like?"

"Ok."

But, shit, was she a goer – though for some perverse reason she would never take her boots off. Never mind, though, leather always did turn me on and it was never long before she stripped everything else off and we were at it like rabbits.

I remember one evening I picked her up from outside Southend Victoria station and we drove out to a pub in the country, somewhere near Battlesbridge. She was gagging for it and wouldn't even let me finish my first shandy, so we left long before time was called and went looking for somewhere quiet to park up.

Farmers are bastards these days, they put barbed wire and other obstacles across the entrances to their fields to keep the likes of you and I off their land. But we found a gap in a fence and I drove in so you couldn't see the van from the road.

We spent the evening adding at least six new variations to the Kama Sutra and it was around 2 am before my lust for her nether regions was overcome by an even more potent yearning for a nice slab of pizza from the late-night gaff on Southend prom, so we decided to sort our underwear out, get dressed and call it quits for the night.

Not so easy, me old mucka. Our rumping had sunk the van down to its axle in the soft ground and it took me a couple of hours and a lot of loud cursing before I managed to dig the thing out and get it back on the road, almost burning the clutch out in the process. Which reminds me, how many Essex girls does it take to screw in a lightbulb? Answer, Essex girls don't screw in lightbulbs, they only do it in the back of old Ford vans.

However steaming hot it might be, passion alone doesn't work for me. There's more to life than just getting your end away and if the bird can't hold a decent conversation you might as well get yourself a blow-up doll and not have to spend all that money on vodka and orange juices.

The traipse across to Essex started to be a right drag and the mokkers were really put on it when I broke down halfway through the Blackwall Tunnel and caused a traffic jam right the way back to Blackheath.

In any event, there were lots more buses coming down the road and, to quote the old cliché, I had no shortage of lasses wanting to find out if that bulge in me trousers was a nice fat wad of money or if I really was glad to see them.

Of course, it wasn't long before the old one-eyed trouser snake betrayed me and I'd put a bird up the duff.

I should have taken notice of the graffiti on the condom machine: "Buy me and stop one! – Buy two and be one jump ahead!" it read with the wisdom of Solomon.

I'd actually 'ad me eyes on a nice bit of skirt called Diana. I even managed to get her to go to the flicks with me a couple of times, but it was like the National Lottery – I kept buying the tickets but my numbers never came up.

So it was that I ended up with Maggie. I met 'er in a local boozer, the Woodhouse, up on Sydenham Hill. My pals and I had gone there looking for student dental nurses from the nurses' home next door but I ended up with a building society counter clerk instead! After a couple of snifters she was anybody's and I got my end away that very first night, while her folks were akip upstairs, which added to the excitement.

I can't really say I was in love but she was a bit of an eye-catcher, with nipples that somehow managed to stick out prominently even if she was wearing an inches thick Aran-wool sweater. She could do a turn as well. In fact, she was a bit of a nympho if truth be known: hot enough to give a hard-on to a snowman.

Of course, I remembered all those biology lectures at school and we took precautions. In fact, I cut down on my consumption of ciggies so I'd have enough dosh to buy plenty of rubber johnnies ("Yes, Mr Barber, I do need 'something for the weekend' please, and I better have a spare packet for in the week!").

Blagger that I am, I quickly sussed out that I could even get contraceptives free from the local family planning clinic, though I was always a bit iffy about that, just in case I bumped into one of my exes there and discovered that it weren't no pillow stuck up her jumper but a sprog on the way that she could prove belonged to me.

Inevitably, though, one steamy night I didn't have any johnnies with me, we did it bare-back and Bob's your uncle, Maggie was in the family way.

Having been brought up proper, I did the decent thing, took Maggie down to H Samuel to choose a ring and when our feet at last touched terra firma they found themselves walking down the aisle to the ominous tones of "Here Comes The Bride".

Her old man was a tough old bastard, built like a brick shit-house; fancied himself as a bit of a villain, a local 'face' – though most of it was just front and, in fact, as I soon sussed out, he was all piss and wind. Anyhow, he had disliked me from day one. He collared me in the bog at the local church hall where we had the wedding reception and laid into me: "You treat her right or I'll fucking 'ave yer," he hissed, glancing down at my family jewels and threatening, with one of those Jerry Lee Lewis evil-eye stares of 'is: "I've heard about you and all your other birds, sonny. Well, if you put that lot where it shouldn't be I'll saw your nuts off with a rusty razor blade." Succinct and to the point was our Rob.

I buttoned my fly and left, knowing exactly where I stood and, as a result, resisted that seemingly irresistible urge to take the pretty little bridesmaid with the great arse round the back of the vicarage for a good seeing to. I spent the rest of the evening being suitably attentive to Maggie and minding my Ps and Qs.

He said all the expected nice things about me in his wedding speech – odd, isn't it, some old prat gets up on his feet to mumble a speech he doesn't really want to make to a bunch of people who would rather not have to listen – but I knew my card was marked. I was never exactly flavour of the month. The in-laws made that simple fact perfectly clear to me at every opportunity.

Even Rob's trusty rusty razorblade couldn't have cut through the atmosphere and it didn't help that, with me being brassic as usual, we couldn't afford a place of our own and were camped out, Maggie, me and the lump, in the in-laws' spare room, with a mattress on the floor among assorted cardboard boxes of dodgy gear which Rob liked to brag he had 'alf inched but which, in reality, he'd been conned into buying and could not offload onto anyone else.

Of course, we should have had Maggie's old room but while we were on our honeymoon – yes, you've guessed, seven nights at Butlin's in Bognor – one of her younger sisters moved her gear in and claimed squatter's rights. I wonder if she'll be so quick to jump into Maggie's grave?

NEW DOORS FOR OLD

By the time baby Michelle was four-months-old, things were at the point among us adults where one or other of us was gonna find weed killer in their tea. We were all getting on each other's tits and were starting to argue about stupid, petty little things like who'd left that soggy tea-bag on the drainer and who'd pebble-dashed the bog. We were desperate to find a gaff of our own. We had already been to the council but were only offered bed and breakfast accommodation.

Believe me, those places were the pits. If you'd housed a dog like that you'd find the RSPCA coming down on you like a ton of bricks. I thought to myself: "Well, I ain't 'aving that".

I was told about a one-bedroom council flat that had been unoccupied for some time, so I went to have a butchers at it. While it was a bit basic and on a fairly rough estate, it looked like it only needed a lick of paint and some tender loving care to make it habitable. It would only be a short-term haven but at least it would enable us to get our first foot onto the housing ladder. A window had been left open, somewhat conveniently, and I climbed in to have a gander – nearly amputating my wedding tackle in the process.

Fortunately, the electricity and gas had not yet been disconnected, the only problem being that the street door was secured like Fort Knox. It had three locks on it: two Chubb deadlocks and one Yale-type lock. Fuck me, it would have taken someone with an Oxford University honours degree in bank robbery to open that lot. The only way for me to cross my home-to-be's threshold in the time-honoured fashion, Maggie in my arms, was to take the frame out and remove the door completely! So that's what I did.

The next day we started moving bits and pieces into the flat and temporarily secured the door. I found a pile of dusty letters concerning rent arrears strewn inside the letterbox. It was plain as the boil on yer bum that the council was not even aware that the flat was empty. So the next day I went over to the housing offices, which were situated on the far side of the estate.

I asked if I could report a repair that needed doing and was directed to the appropriate department. I gave the name of the tenant to whom the letters had been addressed. How I got away with being Mr Obuko Adojo I'll never fathom!

I told them that the flat had been broken into while we'd been away for the weekend and complained that the property was not secure and all our gear was likely to go walkabout if they didn't do something about it, and double quick pronto.

The rather wimpish looking clerk, who didn't seem to know his arse from his elbow, said he would make sure this would be treated as an emergency repair and someone would call within 24 hours to carry out the work. "What a diamond result!" I remember thinking as I walked way: "What a div! No, he can't be that stupid. Surely he's not going to send someone around to fix it?"

Blimey, this geezer is depriving a village somewhere of a much needed idiot.

Sure enough, the very next morning a council carpenter turned up. He got a tape measure from the depths of his tool bag and starting measuring up the door and frame and told me he'd be back within the hour with a suitable replacement.

"Cor, what a blinding council this is!" I thought, as I dragged long and deep on me roll-up. Bang on time for a cuppa and a rich tea biscuit, the chippy returned with everything: new frame, new door and new locks too. He was one of those old fashioned geezers who takes real pride in his work and spent the best part of the afternoon fitting everything, spot on. By 5 pm he was handing me a shiny new set of door keys and left, waving aside the five-pound tip I offered him for a task well done. What a gent, and what a wonderful job he had carried out. We were nice and secure as a condom on an elephant in our new home. I felt like Edmund Hilary planting that flag at the top of Everest. In short, I'd had a right result.

The next day – I'm sure they have since marked it in their annals as the blackest date in their history – I helped the council open the first of many much worn buff folders on me by notifying the appropriate department that we had taken up residence in their flat. My little family was now their responsibility, fair and square.

We managed to get re-housed four months later, firstly because, since we were now living in one of the council's properties, albeit as squatters, we had made ourselves firmly their responsibility, no probs, and also because we had a young baby, which gave us a slightly higher priority in getting re-housed.

Yes, I'd jumped the queue but I felt justified. I had only squatted in the first place because there was no way I was going to subject my wife and nipper to the awful conditions of the bed and breakfast dump we'd been offered. I was learning fast how to play the system but I hadn't yet cottoned on that they keep re-writing the rule-book, the crafty turds, and you have to be well on your toes if you want to keep one jump ahead of them.

A JAR OF COCKROACHES
FOR THE COUNCIL

Eventually we were allocated a two-bedroom flat in an awful tower block in Camberwell – "Asbestos Towers" they should have called it. The sun must have been shining exceptionally brightly the day we went to look at it because the drum didn't seem at all bad, even if the lift was being used by families who believed they should have two kazies and that this could serve as their second one.

It was, though, a legal tenancy and my name was written in blood on the front of the rent book. Unlike previously, when I didn't really have a leg to stand on, me plates of meat were now planted firmly on the floor and I had rights as solid as the Bank of England vaults. When my rent book was issued to me it had a copy of the tenancy agreement in it. I read it thoroughly, once, twice, three times for luck, to ensure that I fully understood every twist of the rules and regulations.

I just love reading the small print and long ago learned that the essence of winning disputes is to know every inch of the ground you are standing on – an approach which, if it was good enough for Monty against the Afrika Corps, is good enough for me against all the little Hitlers I come up against in my frequent brushes with authority.

Unfortunately, I had to deal with the same housing office where I had asked for the door of my squat to be repaired, which meant they were always on guard against me pulling a stroke. They might have been thick, but not that thick. On the other hand, like most bureaucrats, they worked to patterns as predictable as an 'East Enders' script and I'd quickly learned to read their card. We'd even got onto first name terms and I knew how to butter them up, pretending an interest in the things they like talking about, which are mainly bingo, what has been on the box and isn't it terrible all these spongers who they have to deal with?

I was a frequent visitor – surely qualifying for the council's equivalent of air-miles with my regular attempts to sort out minor niggles, like people piling rubbish up outside my garage (which I wasn't paying rent for anyway!) or why the rubbish chute was always blocked. "If at first you don't succeed, try, try, try again (and, if needs be, once more after that)" is the guiding principal of dealing with councils.

God help those who are too old or infirm to call in person – BT must just love the money they clock up when such people are held in phone queues waiting for attention or for an answer to some simple query: like "How many council officials does it take to replace a light bulb?" to which even I can provide the answer: "Three: one to hold the bulb and two to turn the chair round and round."

Now, as my reading of the tenancy agreement had taught me, there's a very strict council rule that you are not allowed to take in sub-tenants, so imagine my dismay – law-abiding soul as I am – when midway through what was one of those very rare long, hot summers, a family of cockroaches resisted the temptations of all those Thomson holiday brochures and decided to chill out in our flat instead of flying off to the sun.

'The cockroach squatters' is what I called them. There were young, brash yobbo ones, full of bravado, and old, geriatric Saga-lout ones who limped across the floor with their Zimmer frames. And they had kids too; lots and lots of kids...

Like everyone who goes on holiday, their prime concern, apart from grabbing all the sunbeds, was to get their end away. Within a week they had multiplied and within a month there were hundreds more of 'em, the oversexed little buggers! Their main abode was in the no-doubt comfortable environs of the heating cupboard, which probably had five-star rating in bug-speak. They must have enjoyed quite a social life and only seemed to come out to take the breeze at night. I'm a bit of an insomniac, so when I used to go to bed at four o'clock in the morning it was like treading on a trail of Rice Crispies on my way to the pit.

I had dropped in and reported this to the council more times than I have fingers and, as per usual, there were two chances of getting something done: one beginning with "fat", the other with "no".

The only response I did manage to extract was: "We have reported this problem to the environmental health department and they should be in touch with you directly." But, of course, I never heard a dickybird.

When I tried to phone environmental health, the number was always engaged. Nobody would tell me where their offices were situated or I would have dropped in to pester them face to face.

By now, Michelle was about a year old and at that stage in life where she was crawling all around the place. In fact, there was no stopping her adventurous little ways. I didn't need to waste money at Toys 'R' Us. She had lots of fascinating little playthings readily to hand. Trouble was, they were all dirty brown colour, hard-shelled, had six legs and scurried across the floor.

I don't think I was being unreasonable in thinking that the council should have got their act together a bit quicker on this one. The authorities are off the mark sharp enough to move diddycoys on – even when they aren't doing anyone any harm – so what about my illegal immigrants?

I had already bought all of the every-day insecticides you can think of from the local supermarkets but they had as little effect as a can of Tennants Export has on a hardened Glasgow Rangers' fan. Yes, you've guessed it, I thought to myself: "No, I ain't 'aving that. Why should I tolerate my daughter being exposed to such unhealthy conditions?" I don't know exactly what it is that cockroaches carry but it can't be anything that's any good.

I decided to make an appointment with my housing officer, who was always off sick or, when in the office, was never available. That's another thing that really pisses me off. Council staff never have the same job for long. They always seem to be playing musical chairs with each other, moving to other jobs, and then you have to wait three months before a replacement takes over and it takes two or three appointments before you suss out where they are coming from and how you can get them on your side in the eternal fight against the system.

As I couldn't get the appointment that I wanted and was just being given the run around, I decided I had to do something that would make them listen – so I got a big coffee jar and placed a dozen or more prime and juicy cockroaches in it. Everyone else's Safeway or Tesco bag contained something for tea. My carrier bag was a natty green one, with a gold Harrod's logo on it, but it wasn't holding anything from the food hall – unless roaches now count as an exotic delicacy.

Deciding to have one more try at doing things the normal way, I went in to the office, leaving my little 'lodgers' in the car. I went through the normal process of having my name and address taken, being given a ticket and being kept waiting for about two hours, reading from cover to cover the same dog-eared old copies of 'Woman's Own' and 'Country Life' I'd read on my previous visit… and the visit before that.

Getting increasingly wound up by the minute, I eventually demanded at the desk for a fixed appointment to be made for my flat to be fumigated. The bird on the counter flicked her gum from one cheek to the other, rolled her eyes in disdain and told me, without even making an effort to try, that she couldn't get through to the department concerned. And as there wasn't a housing officer for my block, there was nothing she could do about it and I'd have to come back some other time. She insisted that the housing officer was the only one who could authorise the work to be done. Oh dear, here we go again!

I went back to the car and got my little friends. I then

made my way back to the reception desk and simply removed the lid and tipped them all out on to the counter.

Boy, did those little creatures move! They were scuttling off in all directions. The poor girl on reception rocked back on her chair in shock – the most movement she'd shown all afternoon. A real minging bit of skirt, a right Doris, she struck me as a totally lazy, not to say, dozy cow. I'm sure the only way her boyfriend would ever know she was having an orgasm would be if she dropped her chips! But she made more movement in those five seconds than she'd made in weeks.

Fighting to keep a straight face, I told her: "You can have these for starters, luv. I'll go 'ome and get some of their buddies, if you like, and you can see how much you will enjoy working with them from nine to five. I have to live with them 24 hours a day – and they're in rent arrears!"

Well, this certainly made those people get their act together. After the receptionist plucked up the courage to get down from the chair she had climbed up on, giving me a nice flash of 'er knickers in the process, she beat a hasty retreat for the inner sanctum and returned promptly with the manager, a Mr Jackson. This character was a man of my previous unhappy acquaintance who somehow managed to combine the experience of youth with the energy of old age.

Now Jacko was not a very happy bunny at all but soon sussed that I had him by the short and curlies. He kept trying to tell me he wasn't going to be brow-beaten by the likes of me but nevertheless eventually promised that someone would visit my gaff and get my problem sorted pronto the next morning. He lived up to his word. I guess he wasn't going to run the risk of my organising visits by coach parties of my little chums.

The council office was closed for three days while the environmental health team fumigated the place but they'd been round to my drum first, so I reckon they got the message that I was becoming very serious. In fact, the first thing the workman said to me was: "Cor, they've 'ad some right nutter down at the town hall. He was going barmy, dropping cockroaches all over the place. The staff there were shitting themselves. We've 'ad to send a right little army of our lads down there to sort 'em out. There's millions of 'em crawling round all over the gaff."

"Funny," he added, with a quizzical look on his face, "the geezer had the same surname as you."

It's interesting, though. Somehow, the council didn't have to go on no waiting list to get their place done and dusted in double quick time.

I must say, once the bug squad got into gear they were brilliant, like the team in that 'Ghostbusters' movie. My flat was fumigated thoroughly and cockroach traps were left all over the place to snaffle any walking wounded.

They even gave me a large can of instant killer spray which was very effective against the few hardy souls holding out in the vain hope that the cockroach Seventh Cavalry was on its way to the rescue.

My ploy had been simple. The best way to get genuine sympathy and real action is to give someone else a taste of what you are up against. They didn't like my little cockroach invasion. I guess they reckoned the roaches would soon be demanding their own keys to the executive loo and it just wouldn't do, having them invade the mayor's privacy each time he went to point Percy at the porcelain. The things you have to do to get things done, I don't know!

"C'MON MAVIS, BRING THE KIDS—WE'RE LEAVING! THIS PLACE IS INFESTED WITH HUMANS!"

I WANT MY FLAT & I'LL DO ANYTHING TO GET IT

I suppose it was inevitable that the marriage wouldn't last. It wasn't that I didn't fancy Maggie. She had a cute little bum and two big bouncers and she bonked like a rabbit. She claimed once to be "all woman", and I told her "Yeah, I know! I always have to get your two friends on the guest list as well when we go clubbing."

The trouble was, though, that I had roving eyes – and I didn't put her above putting it about either. In any event, she often seemed to put the phone down a bit sharpish and then go all red in the face when I came into the room and, by the same token, I was playing fast and loose with every bit of skirt I could lay me eyes on. We tried putting another bun in the oven but while our second little girl, Tracy, was just as cute as the first one, it didn't stop us from drifting apart.

At this distance in time, I can't quite remember if I stomped out on my own accord or if she showed me the door. Whatever, I went off in a right huff and broke the habit of a lifetime by sinking a few swift ones down at the local boozer.

You might have heard the expression: "Crying in his beer" – well, I was throwing a right moody and the tears dribbling down my cheeks meant the Fosters was even more watered down than usual.

I got pissed off that I couldn't pull a bird in consolation, well, maybe I could have done, but the only ones in the pub at the time were right old slappers. What's more, I couldn't use the car as I was juiced up well over the top, so I walked down to Camberwell and checked into a grotty local hotel (£25 quid a night and all the bed bugs you can stand) and spent the rest of the evening pulling my pudding instead of pulling birds.

My old Ma would give me a right earache for leaving Maggie, so I couldn't slope off home to her. Uncle Alf had just shacked up with a new bit of fluff who didn't think too much of me, so I wouldn't be welcome there, and I couldn't afford the penthouse suite at the Dorchester, so I decided I needed to find a flat of my own – and pretty sharpish.

There was no way I was going to go private. For starters, I couldn't afford it and, secondly, I reckoned I was the council's responsibility. According to the tenancy agreement we had with them, and I quote: "The Council shall (within six months) provide suitable accommodation for the party who leaves the dwelling house as a result of breakdown of the relationship" I was, then, clearly their responsibility as, besides my rights under the tenancy agreement, I had lived in the borough for more than two years.

There it was, all cut and dried, in black and white, small print and all. So, Bob's yer uncle, I went to my local council offices and presented myself as being homeless. I explained my circumstances and reminded them of the tenancy agreement's terms – but they blankly refused to re-house me, the tossers.

Instead, I was given a list of bed and breakfast telephone numbers and advised to call them. "I think I've been down this route before," I mused. I shovelled all my loose change into the public telephone round the corner but all of the places on the list were full and not accepting any new people, and they kept referring me back to the council. And, of course, I still got absolutely nowhere with them – everyone just kept passing the buck. I was going round and round like a fairground ride on a bank holiday Monday.

I ended up swallowing my pride and going back to my mum's for a few days. I got a bit of an ear-wigging off her at first but the old dear was more than happy to have 'er favourite son-and-heir put his slippers back under the bed in the spare-room. But if I had stayed there for any longer the council would simply have deemed me no longer homeless and forgotten all about me. Anyway, I had a look around a few local council estates, searching for empty flats – and I found plenty of them. It amazes me as to why these places stay unoccupied for so long, especially as there is always a shortage of homes in the London area.

Well, I soon found out about a lovely two-bedroom flat standing empty in a nice quiet block back on the former LCC estate where I'd grown up on Dog Kennel Hill, in East Dulwich.

The next day I went round in the morning to view the place and, when I got there, you wouldn't believe that the door hadn't been shut properly. Conveniently I had a spare lock and key in my pocket – I wonder how they got there? I also had a little electrical screwdriver. I removed the existing lock with a great deal of trouble because the screwdriver wasn't really big enough for the task.

I seemed to be making a bit of a racket and was fumbling 'cause I was scared someone might suss out what I was up to. And then the next-door neighbour came out to see what was going on. He went to the rubbish chute with just an empty fag box, just so he could investigate what the noise was. I said hello to him and he asked me what I was doing.

"The Council gave me the wrong keys, so I'm putting a new lock on the door," I told him. I then introduced myself by adding: "I'm your new neighbour. The name's Martin. Pleased to meet you."

A good old stick – the sort who will proudly tell you how he fought for his country – George proved quite friendly, so I told him I was having a bit of trouble with the screwdriver, at which he went indoors and got me a better, brand-new one, which still had the B&Q price sticker on it.

He even helped me fit the new lock! I didn't see much point in telling him that I was squatting there and trying to explain that it was the only option left in order to resolve my problem of finding somewhere to live, and that otherwise I would be on the street joining the cardboard box community and qualifying for a cup of soup from the Sally Army brigade. Better to let him assume I was legit.

I made some calls and arranged for the gas and electricity to be put back on, which was easy because I was already a customer from the marital home so I just said I had another place I wanted to be connected. I then went and purchased a Doberman Pincher dog and moved in. I remember when I first took the mutt home I was terrified of it. I had two ham rolls in a paper bag and as I began to eat one of them the dog started growling at me. He was quite insistent that he wanted the rolls for himself, so I locked him in the room with them and let him rip them into slobber-covered chunks and scoff 'em down, bag and all.

I moved my bed and my portable telly into the flat. They were all I had to my name, unless you count a couple of back issues of *Fiesta* and a can of past its sell-by-date Foster's lager. I bought a secondhand Baby Belling cooker and ate loads of hot rice pudding straight from the can. Then I informed the council where they could get in touch with me if they wanted to. They left me there for over a year and then, all of a sudden, the shit bags wanted to evict me.

Within that year I had become friendly with all of my neighbours, especially when Brutus – for that was the dog's name – took me for a drag through the park. For some reason, though, all the regular passers-by disappeared from the pavement as soon as the brute and I hit the street.

I even got a petition up and all the neighbours put their monnikers on it, stating they had no objections to me staying on as a tenant. I did blag a bit by telling most of them that the council themselves had put me there on a temporary basis. There was no point in bragging that I was actually a squatter.

When I went round doorstepping all the people in the block with the petition they were all happy to sign it, apart from one old biddy – but my dog wanted to eat her, so I could understand why she was somewhat reticent about helping. I don't think taking Brutus around with me had any influence on whether the rest of the people signed or not but I did notice that most of them preferred to talk to me through the letterbox.

I even offered to pay the council all of the back rent from the day I had moved in there but they still went ahead and set the process in motion to sling me out on my ear 'ole.

Down I went to the office the day before the eviction to see what they were doing for me but the stuck-up old tart who dealt with me peered disdainfully over her specs and just wouldn't tell me anything, apart from: "You are illegally occupying a council property and until you are homeless we have no obligation to re-house you."

No wonder they had left me alone for a year! Talk about going round in circles. When I was homeless and not squatting they would not re-house me, as I wasn't high enough on the list and when I was squatting they said I didn't count as homeless. Talk about Catch 22! It seemed I just could not win either way. I was then served with an official eviction notice from the council which in posh words told me to sling my hook.

Then the bailiffs come round with the carpenters to chuck me out and board up the flat so nobody else could jump in behind me, but I had already packed my stuff into my Escort van (black fading to grey, with three hubcaps missing and a dodgy MOT) and I just gave them the keys when they arrived.

Three men in suits and wearing moody Ray-Ban sunglasses, had turned up in a beaten-up old Ford Transit. They reminded me of the Blues Brothers, or a crew from one of those low-rent gangster movies that feature Vinny Jones, but in this case there were three of them and they looked pathetic rather than hard: more a case of lock, stock and a smoking exhaust.

I went straight down to the council and demanded to be re-housed, but that old cow cocked a deaf 'un and totally ignored me. She kept calling people who had walked in after me up to the counter, and that really got my goat.

I went outside the building to my van and got my quilt and two pillows, returned to the office and made myself comfortable in a nice warm corner by the radiator. I intended to spend the night there, well, not really – but I wanted them to think that I did. I drew a bit of attention to myself with the members of the public, in fact I think they thought I was a raving nutter, about three sandwiches short of a picnic.

The staff behind the counter were right amused and thought I had totally lost it as I laid my duvet and pillows out on the floor and started making my bed up, with my pillows positioned to prop up my head. I set my alarm clock, got under the covers and whilst laying down noticed that they had loads of photographs in big frames all around the walls, depicting happy families on the local housing estates. On close examination, one of the photos turned out to be of my family and myself, when I was a baby in my mother's arms; I couldn't believe it. I could see this being useful ammo in the battle of words which was sure to ensue!

When it got to twenty past five they starting getting a bit worried. I wanted them to believe that I had no intention whatsoever of leaving. I was homeless and I was their responsibility, so it was up to them to deal with me – after all, they had evicted me and turfed me out on the streets when I was quite cozy in my little squat!

The porter – a right bleedin' Jobsworth – came up to me and asked me to leave, as he wanted to lock the main door. I said, "Are you waiting to go home?"

He replied: "Yes".

"At least you have one to go to," I fired back, adding: "I'm staying here tonight, me old China. I ain't got nowhere else to go. I'm certainly not kipping in my van. It's right brass monkeys outside; too bloody cold for me. At least this place is nice and warm. Bring me a cuppa in the morning, mate. Just one lump please, and a choccy digestive if you can rustle one up. Oh, and turn the lights out when you go, please."

Well he weren't in no mood to tuck me in and read me a bedtime story but went off with the right hump to notify the duty manager, who was sat in his office behind the counter, keeping well out of the way and hoping the problem would just disappear which, of course, it was not about to do.

The last members of the public, a right motley crowd of dossers, spongers, no-hopers and a few genuine hardship cases like me, were leaving the gaff and giving me their vocal support as they left. There were two or three staff finishing up what they were doing and from the looks on their faces I could tell they were thinking: "Blimey, he's a right head case!".

When they had done with shuffling their last bits of paper, they pulled down the blinds on the counter, on each of which was a sign which read pointedly: "Position Closed" (in other words: "Piss off!").

One window stayed open all the time though, with the remainder of the staff all peeping through to see what was going on.

The manager eventually came out of one of the side doors and stood at the foot of my make-shift bed, looking down at me, and asked nervously: "What do you think you are doing?"

I replied: "I'm moving in mate, I've got nowhere else to go, so I might as well live here." He then asked me to leave, to which I said: "Look mate, I've been here since nine o'clock, you've had plenty of time to sort some accommodation out for me, even if it's just some bed and breakfast dive. It's you lot that made me homeless by evicting me and it's up to you to sort it out. That list you gave me this morning was a right waste of time, so get your act together."

He came on at me like a limp-wristed Mothercare bouncer, snapping back in a voice that lacked any real conviction or authority: "If you don't leave now I'll have to call the police."

I think he was under a misguided impression that I was going to run out scared. I just said: "Go on then, call them, I could do with some company." I knew he could have me slung out but simply wanted to inconvenience him for as long as possible and put him to a bit of trouble that might jack the bastard into some action in getting me a drum.

The police arrived and there was no real hassle at all. In fact, they were quite good about it. They understood my situation and at least they listened to what I had to say. I had not acted violently or abusively, so there was no real concern on their part. They almost felt sorry for me but still insisted that I left as, according to them, I was technically committing a breach of the peace.

I remembered having done a bit of research about the ins and outs of that one, so I decided to leave without too much fuss as I knew I didn't really have a leg to stand on, any more than I had a flat to live in. As I was being escorted out of the building by the coppers I shouted out to the manager: "I'll be here in the morning, as soon as you open!".

The minutes had wizzed past and I think it was about half seven by the time I left, so that must have made the council crew happy, having to stay so late and miss 'Coronation Street' before they could lock up.

I then decided that more drastic action was going to be needed, so the next day I decided to go into the office at about 9 am, stayed until 2 pm, nipped off for some pie and mash (with liquor, of course) and then returned at 3 pm. During that morning I had noticed a workman busy fitting an entry-phone system on the main door of the office – I don't know if that had anything to do with me or not but I had my suspicions.

Walking through reception I noticed an instant reaction from the staff, who were talking amongst themselves and pointing at me, probably wondering what was going to happen next. Well, I had plenty in store for them, believe me.

When I got to the main seating area, right in the corner was a very large cast iron hat-stand with an umbrella holder on the lower half. I had seen this on previous visits to the office and had my plan of action fully formed in my mind. I reached into my pocket and produced a proper set of metal handcuffs I had acquired from an army surplus store – well, you don't expect me to confess that I bought them in a sado-masochism shop on King's Road, do you?

With a very theatrical flourish, I applied one part of the

handcuff to my wrist and the other to the hat-stand and clicked them together.

I had already written my demands out on a piece of paper and had them in my pocket. I was not noticed immediately, although I didn't really do it that sneakily.

Very shortly an announcement came over the Tannoy: "I'm afraid that the office will be closing early today. Would all members of the public please leave the building." At this point it was time to be noticed, so waving my Big Issue to draw attention, I started yelling: "Help the homeless!"

Things were getting serious. I was on a buzz and I wasn't in a mood to take prisoners.

The senior manager came out this time; a long, tall streak of piss with shoes polished so you could see yer face in 'em, and an acid-drop expression which could bite its way through reinforced concrete. Well, he seemed to have been born without the ability to smile at the best of times but now he really went into one. You could see the veins sticking out on his neck and he went purple with rage when he saw me attached to the hat-stand with my shiny pair of handcuffs! He asked me why I had done it, so I produced my written list of demands. The first one was my insisting on seeing the top man, his boss, the infamous Mr Johnson of Housing (who is said to have once told a deputation from the homeless: "Well, I don't know about you lot, but I've got a home to go to").

Somebody had called the Old Bill. This time two panda cars turned up, and four policemen from Sun Hill, well, actually from Peckham, stormed through the reception area like they were after some IRA bombers or something. Then they saw me handcuffed to the hat-stand and they just started laughing fit to piss themselves. Old bollock chops Johnson didn't think it was at all funny though.

It was the council as an institution I was really getting at but I didn't mind winding old Johnno up like a good 'un, 'cause he was a right slimey git, so far up his own arse he could brush his teeth from the inside.

The coppers asked me where the key was, so I told them I didn't have it. Naturally they didn't believe me and searched my pockets but they never found the key, which was actually tightly clenched between the cheeks of me bum.

One of the rozzers was on his portable radio reporting back to the station:

"Yes, we have a male handcuffed to an iron hat-stand," trying to keep a straight face as he spoke. "He has no key, so will you ask a unit to attend with a set of bolt croppers?" he added.

There seemed to be some confusion over the radio as to who had handcuffed who. Another two officers arrived with the bolt croppers about 20 minutes later. They were in stitches; they hadn't had such a giggle since the sarge accidentally set his moustache on fire. They thought the whole thing was hilarious. They cut the handcuffs down the middle and removed me from my bondage with some crack about the masochist who asked the sadist to whip him, to which the sadist replied: "No!".

I was then escorted to a police van and, on the way out, turned to Johnson and said with as cheeky a grin as I could muster: "I'll see you in the morning then, squire."

They took me to Peckham nick, but before we got there we had to stop off at the local fire station to have the remainder of the cuffs removed. They had special cutting equipment on hand to do the job. One of the coppers was a bit of a comedian and told the firemen that they'd found me cuffed to a bedstead in a knocking shop. I was then formally arrested for a breach of the peace, and was given a right bollocking by the desk sergeant before being released with a caution two hours later.

I went back to my van, which was still parked outside the council offices. I moved it right onto the forecourt and stayed in it, freezing my bollocks off, until the morning with only a flask of half-warm coffee to keep me company. When they opened the office doors at 9 am I was their first customer. I had to wait a while to get inside the building as the security geezer recognised me from all the kerfuffle the previous day and wouldn't let me in. I hid round the corner and waited for someone to come out before I could gain access, slipping in before the door snapped closed.

When I eventually got into the building, the young girl on reception wrote down all of my details, in between filing her nails, twiddling her earrings and taking swigs of coffee. Everything was written down on the standard visitor form, without Rita – I presume that was her handle because it was written on her name tag – even asking me for any information as to why I was there. I was given a ticket and told to wait.

They obviously had a quick conflab because, at 9.15 am, the manager called me in to his office where he told me: "We are offering five flats to families today. If one of them refuses the offer, then we will offer the flat to you instead".

I tried to find out where the flats were but he just wouldn't give me any solid information. All he did mention was that they were called 'D-Squats'. This meant that they had evicted squatters in the morning and would let the property out the same day. At least this made sense as at last they seemed to be trying to fill places up as soon as they came empty, rather than leaving them uninhabited for months on end as my old squat had been before I took it over.

Fortunately, whilst I was waiting in reception – my temporary new home! – a young geezer came in, really unhappy with an offer that had been made to him, his wife and baby. He refused point blank to take what he described, rather graphically, as "a right shit hole". So it was that I was later that day offered a two-bedroom flat on the worst estate in the area. I signed for it anyway. I wasn't really in a position to refuse it.

It proved to be not just a "right shit hole" but a total five-star shit-hole, so I understood why the family earlier had refused it! Whoever had been there before me had rolled the wallpaper off the walls and knicked all the light fittings when they moved out. I was lucky they hadn't taken the doors and windowframes too. You had to avoid the rubbish bags that were frequently being thrown from the top floor and there always seemed to be cat shit by my doorstep and stale urine in the lifts, on the rare occasions that Mr Otis Elevator was in action. But the flat was mine and my tenancy was 100 per cent kosher. All I had wanted was what I was entitled to and I'd determined that I was going to get it, whatever it took.

Whether they liked it or not, I was clearly the council's responsibility. They had declared policies which were stuck up on the walls of their offices and I meant to ensure that they kept to them and treated me fair and square.

When dealing with a problem like this, it is important to be in possession of all the facts and to understand the potential risks involved if you resort to positive action, as I did. In this particular instance the council had clearly made the rules and regulations themselves and they had even published them in their tenancy agreement booklet, so I clearly had both moral and legal right on my side. I was on pretty much solid ground.

I also knew what risks were involved in the action I took in the council office. I could have wound them up so badly that they'd end up digging their heels in and simply refusing to deal with me any further, so that nothing short of a court injunction would get them to sort things out. Or I could have ended up in court myself, charged with who knows what.

But, as far as police involvement was concerned, I had made discreet inquiries with a copper of my acquaintance, who was based at a police station well out of the area, so I knew that even if I had been charged with a breach of the peace it would have had very little consequence, as this incident would be treated as a minor offence. I must say that on this occasion the Old Bill dealt with me very fairly and the arrest was carried out in a professional manner (which, in my bitter experience, is unusual).

Now, you have to realise that if a police caution is accepted, it is regarded as being tantamount to an admission of guilt and will appear as an entry on a criminal record. Such action by the police simply saves the taxpayer dosh by avoiding the matter going through the time and money-consuming rigmarole of the courts.

I believe that the duty inspector can decide whether to caution or to charge you and the course of action decided on depends on the circumstances of each individual case. Unfortunately all this was not explained to me when I was cautioned, so I learned the hard way, although this type of caution is not overly serious and only represented a small smudge in my copybook.

If the council had not made these well publicised claims to care or specified time limitations for re-housing someone in the circumstances that I was in, I wouldn't have been taking such drastic action. I didn't really want to put everybody to so much trouble, after all, they are only ordinary people doing a crap job for crap money, but it seemed the only way to get what their own propaganda says I was quite clearly entitled to. Sometimes you just have to do whatever is necessary. And, following my time-honoured "I ain't 'aving that" maxim, that's exactly what I did.

Though I have to accept that the world today runs on high-octane bullshit, I still reckon you have a right to keep people to their word. However, misleading propaganda plays a major if often well-disguised role in our everyday lives and when they say "Don't believe everything you read in the papers", I reckon they should be a bit more honest and say "Don't believe anything you read in the papers". I reckon there's lies, damn lies and the tabloids.

To be frank, apart from the tits on page three, I reckon the redtops aren't even good enough to wrap the rubbish in. They paint such an odd picture of the world, making it sound like a right cess-pit when, in fact, apart from the sort of incidents you'll read dotted over my story, it's not really such a bad place.

They try to tell us that bad news is all the public wants to read about but I'm not so sure. The problem is that while any hack with the ability to string a few words together can report on a rape, a murder or a sex scandal and make it sound titivating, it takes a really good writer to pen an entertaining and stimulating piece about the good things in life. As a result, most journalists cop out and write almost exclusively about the seedy side of things.

Wordsworth's poem "Daffodils", for instance, will still be read and will give pleasure in a thousand years time, but yesterday's copy of The Sun is already wrapping fish and chips.

It doesn't have to be that way. Charles Dickens, Mark Twain and Ernest Hemingway all started out as reporters and I bet that if you could bring those marvellous scribes back from the dead and get them to produce a newspaper that only featured good news it would clean up, in every sense.

Being a bit of a leftie at heart – no, re-phrase that, being a total Bolshie bastard – I used to think there was a right-wing conspiracy to keep us in the dark about what's really going on in the world and to make everywhere else sound so terrible while they blew the trumpet of how great their version of dear ol' Blighty is.

My first trip behind the old Iron Curtain, helping my mate Dennis deliver some cut-price electronics' gear to a dodgy importer who happened to be well connected with the party, proved a real eye-opener (he could sell Brylcream to a baldie, could our Den). I thought it would all be black and white (or, rather, grainy grey), raining all the time, with Humphrey Bogart clone-like geezers lingering on street corners, dragging on fag-ends, hats pulled down over their eyes and trying to flog us black market nylons.

It was a real shock to find out that while living standards might not have been great shakes, people in the East could have a good time – or was that all-night party when I sank half a bottle of vodka and pulled Freda, that great bird with the massive knockers and a magic way of twiddling my pubes, just a figment of my imagination?

And what about the night when we got invited to some big state function up on the Baltic coast, just inside Poland, at a place called something like Slupsk, when we all got tanked up and the big fat mayor ended up doing a striptease on top of the grand piano while the pianist tinkled *"The Stripper"*?

It must have been about 2 am when we left to walk back to our hotel in the company of the local police chief and a five-star Polish army general, both in full dress uniform, epaulettes, medals and all. We were all pissed as farts and dying for a pee, so the four of us – two South London likely lads and a pair of Polish big wigs – lined up against a handy wall to offload the potent mix of vodka, Polish brandy and beer we had so injudiciously consumed over the past four or five hours, when around the corner slid a police car.

Two young coppers jumped out and yelled out at us in Polish, with words which I presume were to the effect of: "What the fuck do you think you're doing?"

With that, the police chief span round, his tackle still dangling out of his trousers, raised two fingers, in time-honoured fashion, and shouted back imperiously – in English: "Why don't you fuck off?!" at which they saluted, jumped back in the car and raced off into the night!

A couple of cheapo package holidays in Bulgaria, wife and kids in tow, gave me evidence enough for my own eyes that people and the things they worry about are pretty much the same the world over and that even bureaucrats and party brown-nosers actually like to have fun most of the time. I quickly sussed that, if you look hard enough, you can find plenty of enjoyment being had in even the most grim seeming of places. In fact, it seems to me, the bigger the dump, the better the people are at letting loose and having a right good time. Just look at the Swiss, they live in a paradise where someone comes out early each morning and newly paints the mountains sparkling white, but they are a right po-faced, mardy bunch who never seem happy. On the other hand, I've never had so many laughs as you get with a bunch of Belgian navvies in some shit 'ole mussels and chips emporium. You'll find far more sour-faced people in Shirley Hills or Chislehurst than you ever will down the Old Kent Road

The reality of the world is, I soon decided, certainly different from how the media depicts it all. I've learned that, whatever its faults, this old globe of ours, warts and all, isn't such a bad place as the papers and the politicians would have us believe. So why is it that the latter mob in particular always paint such a bad picture of everywhere else in the world?

Well, I've learned that it's not the conspiracy I suspected, after all, but rather a simple human defence mechanism. I'll explain: should you have cause to phone the local council to complain that your bin wasn't emptied on Friday, as it should have been, it's a lot easier for the bods at the council to get themselves off the hook by saying, "You think, it's bad here? You should try living in Croydon. Their bins never get emptied" than it is to come up with a proper explanation. After all, they know you're not likely to hop on a Connex or Network SouthEast train to Croydon just to see for yourself if they are bull-shitting or not.

At a national level, when somebody has a pop at Tory Blair it's easier for him to claim things are better in Britain than they are anywhere else than it is for him to start addressing the issues.

You might not be able to fool all the public all of the time but if you're a politician up there in the firing line then you're bound to have a crack at fooling most of the public most of the time. I've come to the conclusion that bullshit is in such popular demand these days that they should sell it in cans in your local Sainsburys superstore – and give double points on your reward card.

"ONCE UPON A TIME THERE LIVED A PRINCESS...."

PUTTING HEAT ON THE COUNCIL

Out of wedlock and out of work, I eventually reached rock bottom... and from then on it seemed downhill all the way. But somehow, my life always seems to turn a corner before too long. Maybe it's because I'm a confirmed optimist. No, I'll re-phrase that: I'm an optimistic pessimist.

An optimist buys a lottery ticket convinced he's going to win. If he does, it's no big deal because that's what he expected. If he doesn't then he's right pissed off.

A pessimist is convinced he's never going to win so he doesn't even bother to buy a ticket, and you can't win a race if you don't take the start..

The optimistic pessimist, on the other hand, knows he's not going to win but thinks to himself, "Well, somebody's numbers come up every week, so what the hell, it's only a quid". So he buys a ticket. If he loses he doesn't give a toss because that's exactly what he expected and he shrugs it off, treating it as he would a quid he lost through a hole in his pocket. But if, by a fuckin' miracle, he should win then it's totally unexpected and he gets maximum pleasure, like a pig in shit.

It always helps your passage through life if you can think positively, like the old Irish fella who once told me: "The sun always shines in Ireland. Of course, it's often hidden behind the clouds, but it's always up there shining."

Anyway, I found a new job and soon had a new bird on the firm, and I was able to shack up at her place at least three times a week. She was a cracker, you could take your socks off and just paddle in those incredible eyes.

Nor was she my only option. I had a little Chinese lass on the go as well. One night I told her I fancied a 69 rather than the cocoa she offered and she said: "Piss off! I'm not cooking at this time of night."

Then, when it seemed I was doomed to this wanderer's life, dossing on other people's sofas or sharing someone else's bed, I was at last moved into a council flat of my own – "Ah, home sweet home!" – in April 1992. This move was, as I have explained, entirely kosher, and I had a rent book to prove it.

Stupidly, I thought that all I needed bring along was the dog, pipe and slippers and bliss would be assured. Wrong!

I soon discovered that in the kitchen area there were not one but three gas meters poking out of the floor. It was a right fucking mess. I contacted the gas company to see if I could get the redundant ones removed.

Shit! What a can of worms I was opening 'ere. The gas people visited me and I was advised that the meters were council property and therefore I should get in touch with the local authority to have them removed. So I did.

When the council geezers came round they refused to remove the meters and said I should get in touch with the gas company! Oh dear, here we go again: welcome back to the magic roundabout!

Meter number-one was connected to the heating system (I'll be coming back to that later), meter number-two was connected to the hot water supply and meter number-three was connected to the gas cooker. I couldn't understand why I needed three. I just wanted the two excess ones taken out: I'm not a greedy soul, I just wanted one meter, like everyone else has. After all, it was only a one-bedroom flat. I had intentions of having a fitted kitchen installed one day. The profusion of meters took up lots of space and would clearly create a major problem when fitting new worktop units.

Well, I again got on to the cowboys, oops, I mean the

council, and thought I would have it out with the manager of the maintenance section. After an hour on the phone and talking to just about every department except the one I actually wanted, I eventually got through to the right person.

I patiently explained the whole thing and the boss man said he would arrange for a second visit to assess what needed to be done. An appointment was duly set up.

On the appointed morning I patiently waited in but by noon nobody had turned up. I dived for the phone and started driving them mad, as you do. I was told by some plank that in their book a morning appointment means any time up to one o'clock – which seems bizarre to me as, according to the rest of the world, morning grinds to a halt each day at noon. So I waited until three and then I thought I'd go down to the office and drive them potty in person.

As I went out, there, I spotted a dog-eared card from the council. It was sitting in the wire basket that I had attached to the door to catch the mail. It stated that: "An engineer called and there was no reply. Will you please call the office to make another appointment. Failure to do so within seven days will then cancel the job".

Great! I went straight down to their office and bent the manager's ear severely. As I had been in waiting, I was sure nobody had knocked on my door. The workman must have tip-toed up in his stockinged feet and slipped the note through the letterbox so as not to make it rattle. Or perhaps he timed his call to perfection and arrived just when I was in the bog having a dump. Anyway, the manager promised to have someone back at my premises before end of play that day.

Within an hour an engineer knocked at the door. What a happy man he was! He looked like someone had just knicked the jam out of his doughnut. As he walked through the door he grunted to me: "I've just been pulled off another job to come here," to which I replied: "It's a shame they don't keep to their appointments then, ain't it mate? Would you like a cup of rosy?" I wanted to cheer him up a bit – and boy did the miserable git need it – because I was keen on getting the work done that day and he was the key to that happening.

Well, two of the meters were eventually removed and just one meter was connected for all of the amenities. I then contacted the gas company to replace the remaining meter with a new-style card meter and arranged an appointment with them.

But when the installer had replaced the existing meter with the new one and carried out all of the work, he told me he couldn't turn on the supply, as there was inadequate ventilation in the kitchen area.

He advised me to call the council back in to put a vent in the window: "It must have a constant flow of air," he warned imperiously. He then labeled my meter with a card reading: "DANGEROUS DO NOT USE". Stick a fucking skull and crossbones on it and he couldn't have made the point any more strongly.

What a palaver! I got in touch with the council again and arranged yet another appointment. When the council engineer came around this time he said that the engineer from the gas company should not have disconnected me. He said, the gas man should have just checked for leaks and then reconnected the supply.

I had gone three days without heating, hot water or cooking facilities. I was growing stubble, had begun to pen and ink and was, it seemed, going round in the proverbial circles, heading precisely nowhere except perhaps disappearing up me own bum 'ole. After a lot of ranting on my part, I got the supply switched back on.

A week later, I was out one evening and didn't get home till late. When I returned to the flat it was absolutely freezing. I swear, if I'd taken a piss it would have turned to ice before it hit the pan. I went to the heating cupboard and the heater was off and so was the pilot light, while the boiler was cold as a polar bear's bum. I called the council and told them that the heating system was faulty. A further appointment was made and the engineer said he needed to order a part and it might take a week to arrive.

I called the council every morning of every day and

managed to get the job done within four days. Drive 'em mad, that's what I say! It seems apparent that if you keep ringing up and asking for the same person and really get on their nerves they can't wait to get rid of you, so you get the job done quicker.

To cut a long story short, the supply was disconnected six times by the gas board and reconnected six times by the council. There were 16 separate repairs carried out on the heating system. During all this fiasco the council also put a vent in the kitchen window for me. I didn't realise the dramas that little move would cause. On one memorable occasion the gas board cut the supply off because the vent that the council had fitted in the window was what the gas bloke called 'a closeable vent'. It had a piece of string dangling from each side and evidently this was what made it 'closeable'. The gas people were adamant that for safety reasons the vent must at all times have a constant flow of air so the supply was disconnected again because of inadequate ventilation.

Three days later the council engineer arrived with a pair of scissors in his hands and went straight to the window and cut off the two offending bits of string, so the vent could no longer be closed! I had gone three days without all amenities and then waited in all day for the engineer, just for him to cut a bit of string off. Need I say, I was hopping mad and the gas board still wouldn't reconnect my supply. I was becoming almost suicidal in my frustration but there wouldn't have been any point shoving my head in the oven!

The council works manager managed to avoid me for the next two days, despite my leaving about 20 messages asking for him to call back. I decided to waylay him on his way in to work on the third day. I was sitting outside the works division at 8 am, primed up to have a little chat about this ongoing saga. He could see I was about to lose my rag, so, judging discretion the better part of valour, as they say, he invited me into his office, even offered me a cuppa, and made some feeble excuse about not having been given my messages.

He fobbed me of with some mumbo-jumbo but I felt better that at last I had been given the chance to vent my feelings to a real live person and not just one of those mechanical voices on some answerphone where they compound the injury by playing you tapes of Andrew Lloyd Webber's greatest crap played on the pan pipes.

The supply still wasn't put back on though. I had been disconnected for three weeks, I was living like an animal and I couldn't take it anymore. I drove straight down to the council's main office, which had the works division located in the adjoining building; this meant that all staff used the same car park.

I stormed straight in to reception and demanded to see the housing manager or whoever was the work's manager's boss. They were both conveniently unavailable, natch. That fucking did it. I went outside and moved my car so it was right in the middle of the car park entrance, stopping all the office staff from getting in and stopping the workmen from getting out.

I got out of the car, locked it, and then went back into the office and waited. It was only a few minutes before it all started. I heard horns sounding continuously and cars, vans and trucks were queued up nearly the full length of the road.

A contractor walked in, asking if anyone had parked their car by the gate. I said: "Yes, it's mine, mate, and I'm not moving it until they fix my heating and hot water."

He just walked out with the right hump, he didn't really want to get involved. I went back outside to check that nobody was tampering with the car. As I looked in the car park I saw there were a dozen or more vehicles now lined up waiting to get out. The workmen were all standing in little groups talking to one another. I approached them and was quite polite to them.

I just explained that I had not had heating, hot water or cooking facilities for three weeks and I was not prepared to go without them for any longer and that, as a result, this was a protest action on my part and, sorry for the inconvenience, but I'm not moving for anybody.

It was quite funny actually as they were all happily agreeing with me and said they thought my course of action was justified in the circumstances. It meant, of course, that they couldn't do any work until I had moved, so effectively I was giving them a morning off... on full pay.

I had no intention of moving my car until I had some satisfaction. I returned to the office to find that the receptionist had informed her superior. She called me to the counter and hissed: "If you don't move that heap now, I'll call the police and have it and you removed forcefully."

I kept my call and replied in a quiet tone: "I haven't had any breakfast this morning, my flat is like an igloo, I've had to wash and shave in cold water, and it's been like this for three weeks. I want to see the Manager, NOW PLEASE!"

She stormed off, saying she was going to call the police. I decided I had best go back to the car, and locked myself in it. I was causing absolute chaos and was delighted to find that I had virtually brought the council yard to a standstill.

The gavvers arrived quite quickly in their little noddy cars and told me to get out of the vehicle, but I didn't really want to. The copper said that if I didn't get out, he would arrange for the vehicle to be towed away with me in it. I was losing my bottle a bit and realised I might be sailing into deep shit but, bugger it, this was a shit or bust situation, so I decided to stick to my guns. I repeated that I wasn't getting out of the vehicle or moving it until the council fixed my heating and hot water.

The copper in charge talked to the council people and negotiated with me through my very partially opened driver's door window. It was like one of those hostage negotiation scenes you see on the telly. I was expecting the helicopters and tear gas at any minute.

Someone from the council eventually agreed that if I moved the car they would get the manager to talk to me personally, at which, to everyone's relief, I agreed to park the vehicle out of the way.

I went in to an interview room in the council offices,

where the housing manager and the maintenance manager were waiting for me. I explained that it wasn't a nice way to treat a human being and demanded some action. They agreed that within one hour they would have an engineer at my flat to sort everything out and I would have heating and hot water by the end of the day. Well, credit where its due, their people called round within that time. The bell rang and there were not just one but three engineers at the door, with tools, pipes and parts. They also had two rather big boxes and after I let them in they unpacked two brand-new electric convector heaters which they instantly installed and plugged into the wall socket. This was so I had temporary heat whilst they fixed the system.

It took another two calls before the work was completed. I had even rigged up a hosepipe that I had bought from the local DIY shop for £19 and connected it to my next-door neighbour's taps, bless her, so that I had hot water. It took about an hour just to fill my bath up, but it was better than nothing.

Then the system developed a fault in the switch and the unit would not turn off. By this stage I had had enough. I contacted Corgi, the health & safety organisation which not only sets the standards for gas installations but keeps the national list of registered fully-qualified gas engineers. Indeed, if you aren't Corgi registered then it's illegal to work on gas fitting jobs.

I also got in touch with the manufacturer of the heater unit and the gas company again. I thought it would be a good idea if they all got together and talked with each other, as there was a bad communication problem. Obviously, this way, more would be achieved.

I received a call from the Corgi engineer and he arranged to visit and inspect the system. Well, a lot was achieved by getting this expert involved. His conclusion was that the system should be condemned and replaced as soon as possible.

He found so many defects: for example, the fan had been hot-wired, which meant that it had been running day-and-night non-stop, just burning up electricity at my expense. Also, there was no return air-flue, which meant there could easily have been a build-up of dangerous fumes, and, finally, apart from the ventilator recently fitted in the kitchen, there was no ventilation at all in the flat. To be honest, I'm lucky I'm not a goner.

A site meeting was arranged by me to bring together everyone concerned – and, surprise, surprise, they all turned up. It was like a madhouse. There was Corgi man, the council inspector, the council service manager, the neighbourhood manager and me. Mr Corgi requested a number of items to be fitted to my flat, the others eventually agreed, and then the work began.

Firstly they replaced all of the main gas pipes coming from outside the property. They also replaced all the gas pipes within the property that fed the water heater, the boiler and the cooker. Then they changed the old heating unit for a brand new one. A return airflow was also fitted, with two metal vents that had not even existed before fitted to the heater cupboard door. Vents were also fitted in every main door in the flat, and another non-closeable vent was fitted in the kitchen window while a further large vent was fitted in the wall between the kitchen and the hallway.

It now meant that my heating, hot water and cooking facilities were actually safe to use! My home had been like a building site for two days, resembling a re-fit of the QE2, but at least I now had all my services running and they were in a safe and usable condition.

Ah, but that wasn't the end of it. No way. After all the work had been completed I knew I had to pursue a claim for compensation. After all, I'd been put to a lot of trouble and, you guessed, I wasn't 'aving that.

I had been inconvenienced greatly, my safety had been compromised drastically and I had suffered a great deal of stress due to the whole episode. I had also incurred a great deal of personal expense, whopping up BT's share value in the process with all those phone calls I'd had to make.

I went through all of the council complaint procedures and filled in all the forms necessary to claim for compensation but they offered an insultingly piddling amount in settlement. I guess they were just testing the water, so my final letter was strongly worded and threatened them with legal action. In fact, though, I had already decided at this stage that I didn't really want to involve a solicitor as I would only be adding more expense to my existing list of costs and it would probably have taken years for the case to drag its weary way through the courts.

I decided instead to make a bluff of it and simply wrote directly to the council's legal department. I then followed it up with many phone calls, always making sure I had all the facts to hand.

When I spoke to the person that the council had allocated to deal with me, he seemed surprised that I wasn't planning to use a solicitor. Indeed, he virtually insisted that I would need one, as I needed to submit a document called a "Particulars of Claim", if I was to pursue a claim against them and for some reason he seemed to think that completing this would be beyond my intelligence, the patronising git.

I, on the other hand, insisted that I would be dealing with everything myself and said: "I'll have it on your desk first thing Monday morning."

The whole weekend was spent preparing the papers. I based my key document on the one configured by my solicitors for the action taken against the clutch company (wherein lies a completely different story!). I just changed the words, using 'heating system' instead of 'clutch', and made a few other alterations. I delivered it by hand to the council legal department in a big buff envelope which looked suitably official, like those ones you get from the tax office, where, as you open them, the Chancellor's hand shoots out and goes for your jugular.

I received a reply within two weeks and an appointment was made for me to discuss my claim with them. When I attended the meet, the housing manager was present and the maintenance manager was also there, along with their legal representative. I was sitting there on my own, just me and my Lever-arch file, bursting with all my documentary evidence, reports, job sheets and all of the gas company disconnection notices, not forgetting my receipt for 19 quid for the hose pipe! I was outnumbered, but there was no way I was gonna be intimidated. I felt I was much better prepared than they were, so it was easy for me to sow confusion and get them all flustered.

We all sat round the table and started to talk about adequate compensation.

"After great consideration, the council has decided to offer you £300 in compensation for all your inconvenience," said the man from Snatchit, Grabit and Run, rather pompously, the twat, as if they were being right generous.

I called their buff and simply replied: "I think we should let a court deal with this then. I feel you've wasted my time here today – and the loss of a day's wages will be added to what I am asking for. You know full well what this claim would be worth in damages if I were to issue proceedings against you."

"Well, did you have a figure in mind, Mr Rogers?" asked the housing manager rather nervously. This was a clear indication to me that they wanted to negotiate, so I plucked a figure out the air and asked for £3,500, on the principle that you can always come down but you can't go up.

I knew that this figure wasn't unrealistic if a court were to deal with it. We then haggled a bit and I was then asked to leave the office for a moment while they had a conflab amongst themselves. A settlement was agreed, with me demanding that it be paid within 28 days, as I didn't want to wait six months for the money.

My compensation was to be £2,000, by way of cheque, which was paid within two weeks, so that was the deposit for my new fitted kitchen taken care of, thanks very much. I also got £19 on top for the hosepipe. Oh, and, yes, that extra day of lost wages and the money I had spent on taking a cab to the meeting. Sweet!

Over the months, this complaint had become a very complicated problem to deal with. In a situation like this you must first find out who is actually responsible for what, as a lot of buck passing will go on from one organisation or department to another. There is nothing more time-wasting and frustrating than going off half-cocked and arguing with the wrong people.

The main reason that this case was difficult to sort out was that a number of parties were involved. However, the property belonged to the council, so they were really responsible for all gas appliances in use there.

It was a very good idea to get Corgi involved as they had quite an influence over the council and laid down strict guidelines that should have been followed. If I had not called them in I would probably never have known that my local authority was compromising my safety and would not have realised that my heating unit was wired incorrectly. This could have easily caused an electrical fire. I sometimes wonder if I would be alive to tell the tale if I had not made this timely discovery.

I might sound petty to some people, but why should I, or anyone else for that matter, have to suffer financial loss and huge inconvenience due to someone else's incompetence or negligence. In this case I even worked out to the decimal point how many units of electricity had been used by the electrical fan. Again, why should I pay? I had a proper record of all the days I had to stay in and wait for workmen to turn up (and whether or not they did so), the phone calls, and the letters. You must claim back everything you're entitled to – down to the last penny – then round it up for contingencies.

I still have a rather copious file on this one. It includes copies of all the letters which winged their way backwards and forwards and an itemised computer print-out from the phone company showing all the calls that were made in reporting the faulty gas equipment. There are also copies of the disconnection notices from British Gas, the report from Corgi, my Particulars of Claim, and finally a letter confirming compensation (including payment slip). It still makes happy reading!

If you are going to be a barrack-room lawyer then you

have to know exactly what you are talking about, which is why I took to filling my spare time boning up on law books and case history rather than wasting it on Jeffrey Archer novels.

There's this black guy at our local library who has proved a gem in helping me with all my run-ins with the council. Duncan is amazingly well educated and a fount of information on just about everything – but especially the law, which he studied at university. Tall, willowy even, he dresses immaculately, his shirts white on white – always worn with cuff-links of course – his trouser creases razor sharp and his tie in a perfect Windsor. Posh too: he speaks like the Queen but with a lisp, being rampantly, no, outrageously camp.

Buy him a cappuccino, let him prattle on about his cottaging exploits and who he'd like to shag and he'll repay you by spending hours pouring through books and case studies looking for the answer to whatever little legal problem you might be facing. He's a tenacious bleeder who just will not give up till he's found all the answers. The man's fitted with two buttons: one for "go", the other for "search and destroy"! For the price of that cappuccino he comes a lot cheaper than a lawyer!

If you've got a complex form to fill in and need help, then Duncan's your man. He's also one of those people who seems to know everyone who counts, from local councillors right up to big knobs in the City. If he doesn't know them personally, he certainly knows someone who does.

THE POLYSTYRENE
PACKAGING WORTH £15

If councils are often incompetent and riddled with bureaucracy, retail companies can be downright unfair, rude and, well, pig ignorant. I had a tickle on the gee-gees and was flush with dosh, so I went into an electrical shop in Tottenham Court Road to buy a video-mixing machine for the camcorder which I'd just picked up for a song and was planning to use in my latest failed-business-to-be as a wedding photographer.

I told the shop assistant exactly what I wanted it to do. He came across as a computer geek who knew his onions, so I took his word on it when he advised me on the model that would suit my needs. It cost about £500, a not inconsiderable wedge, but on his recommendation I bought it and took it home. I played with it all weekend, trying to get it to do what I wanted, but I had very little success.

Though I kept ringing the shop for further advice – always being made to feel I was being a pain in the arse and imposing on their valuable time – I still made no progress. I tried all week and by the next weekend I had given up on trying to make it work and had completely gone off the idea. I decided to put everything back in the box and return it to the shop and get my sovs back. I went in and explained that the device was not compatible with my camcorder and was, in any event, far too complicated for a simpleton like me to use.

They offered to swap it for something else but I wanted a full refund. Well, this got right up the shop manager's hooter and he did everything possible to avoid giving me my dosh back. But after a little bit of argument and me quoting word for word from the Sale of Goods Act he began to believe that I was not the sort of person to mess with.

I also mentioned that, according to the law, the goods he sold should be fit for the purpose they were bought for. He then agreed to give a refund but said that he would have to check the goods first. That was fair enough so, of course, I said "Fine."

He took the box out back. Ten minutes later the little shit returned to the counter to advise me gravely that a piece of polystyrene was missing from the packaging. I told him that everything I had taken home was still in the box, but he replied that he would have to deduct £15 for the missing item, which was a piece of polystyrene packing the size of a fag box and worth a few pence.

Yes, you've guessed it, I thought, "I ain't 'aving that". 15 quid for a bit of poxy packaging? You're having a right laugh ain't you? There was no way I was letting him get away with such a rip-off. I protested but he was quite adamant that he was going to stop this amount from my refund, and said firmly: "Until you return the missing piece of packaging, I will not give you your £15 back."

If I'd had the bit of polystyrene at home, which I didn't, it would have cost me a lot more than 15 smackers to jump in a cab, pick it up and get back to Tottenham Court Road before closing time.

Like a lot of tight-wads, he seemed the sort who was only to happy to take dough off the punters but really resented giving it back, even when he knew he had to. He just had to have the last laugh and think he'd pulled a successful stroke.

You will not be surprised to hear that I blew a fuse, threw a mega-wobbly, and started to involve customers in the shop who were on the point of purchasing gear. I also approached new customers who were just coming through the door.

"Don't buy anything from here, they're right rip-off merchants," I told them, adding, "Just look what they're trying to do to me. They want to charge me £15 for a poxy little piece of polystyrene that wasn't even there in the first place."

Of course, people shuffled round rather embarrassed and not a few took to their heels and left. This action really got to the manager and he started shouting at me in a very threatening tone: "Get out of my shop," he barked. I refused to go but at least three singularly unimpressed customers did depart almost immediately, one of whom had at least a grand's worth of camcorder equipment spread out on the counter which he looked like he was about to pay for. Unfortunately for the shop, this customer left without buying as much as an A2 battery. I wonder why?

The manager then started to get a bit aggressive and began waving his hands at me but I still wanted my money back and I wasn't leaving until I got it. The wanker decided to call the police, which was something that I gleefully encouraged as I knew the law was fully on my side. I was still telling my story to various potential customers as they walked through the door. It was hilarious, they walked in, I gave them my patter and they promptly turned around and walked straight back out again, apart from a couple of rubberneckers who were hanging around because they were enjoying the fun.

About 20 minutes later, the police arrived. One officer questioned me, the other dealt with the shopkeeper who by this time had completely blown his fuse. The Old Bill decided I wasn't committing any criminal offence and said that this was a civil matter, but they did ask me to leave the shop. I then told the shopkeeper that I would be standing outside all day and the next day too, until he gave me my full refund.

The police advised him that he should pay me back my £15 as they could remove me from his premises but could not stop me standing outside his shop all day as long as I was not causing an obstruction.

The Verdict?... He refunded me the £15 shortfall and

said pointedly: "Don't ever come back to my shop" – but would I ever want to?

The silly bastard! By trying to rip me off, he'd wrecked his whole afternoon's trade and made himself look a total arse-hole to everyone who passed by. I, on the other hand, had nothing to lose by my action. Ok, some of the onlookers might have thought I was some kind of nutter but they didn't know me from Adam and chances were I'd never cross their paths again.

This whole affair was really a matter of principle on my part. Why should I let old shit for brains charge me good money for something that wasn't even there in the first place and which, in any case, could not have cost more than a few coppers? I didn't really have any idea things were going to have to go as far as they did but I do feel the shopkeeper was really trying to take advantage of me and probably thought that I was not going to argue with him but would back off, just as all too many punters do.

He obviously didn't realise who he was up against. This whole sorry episode probably lost him about £3,000 worth of sales. Was it really worth his while, I wonder?

ONCE MORE UNTO THE BREACH: MARRIED AGAIN

They say we learn by our mistakes. Like bollocks we do! My second marriage was as big a disaster as the first one. Perhaps more so.

Maggie and Shelly were very different, from their hair colour to their bra size to their temperament.

They had one thing in common, though. They both liked going at it like demented rabbits on heat. Shelly was the more adventurous. We tried all the recognised positions then invented some more of our own.

She enjoyed 'aving it off in different places too, like in the kitchen, in the bath, on the stairs and out in the woods. Most of all she liked bonking in the Vectra. Question: how does your wife turn the light off when you're making love? Answer: she shuts the car door.

We met in Mallorca, at El Arenal, and I got my end away on the beach that very first night. It took days to get all the sand out of my bum crack.

She'd been there a week, fighting off a legion of beer-swilling Kraut dickheads, with their mullet haircuts and naff moustaches, so I suppose a good solid South London boy like me seemed a relief. If she'd chosen Magaluf instead then we'd never have met and she would have ended up married to some grocer from Kettering.

We found out we lived just streets away from each other and as soon as we got back to London we moved in together. My divorce hadn't yet gone through and she wasn't too pleased when she found herself cited in the divorce papers.

It was great at first, as these things always are. I don't want to sound all poetic and pretentious but I remember laying awake, late at night, marvelling at the gently arcing curve of her back as she lay sleeping in the half light. She was no pin-up but there was an elfish attraction to her slim, petite form. I'd call her pretty rather than beautiful but that's the kind of sort who turns me on.

Personality is important with me too. She had a great sense of humour, a witty way with words that always made me laugh, though that eventually curdled and became a bitingly cruel tongue that knew just how to hurt… and then some.

She could be a prick-teaser too, using every little movement, every glint in her eye and curl of her lip to make me believe my luck was in, like it was my birthday, then, just as I was about to explode with anticipation, she'd jump out of bed, slipping some clothes on and rushing out for some milk, always for some milk…

When we did get down to it, which was often, it was always bareback, so I suppose pregnancy was as inevitable as death and taxes and pretty soon, just 18 months apart, in fact, we'd knocked out Terry and Sarah, which gave me two more mouths to worry about feeding.

Things were none too easy. The Child Support Agency Gestapo were giving me a lot of gyp and putting the squeeze on me tighter than a boa constrictor on the rampage. I wonder how many other second marriages have been wrecked by the strain of trying to keep up with the demands of the first family?

I found myself working longer and longer hours, sometimes holding down two full-time jobs at a time and doing my usual ducking and diving, wheeler-dealering on the side. I'd get home so knackered that even Michelle Pfiffer standing in front of me starkers couldn't have given me a stiffie.

Even worse, a couple of times I came close to falling asleep halfway through giving Shelly one. I was becoming just about as popular as a ferret in a rabbit warren. The whole thing had gone pants... big time.

We were always short of dosh and to make matters worse still I kept getting phone calls from one of my old flames who still had a crush on me. Never mind that there really was nothing going on – as it happened, I was too cream crackered all the time to get up to any hanky-panky – Shelly convinced herself that I was bonking this other sort with a vengeance.

She took to going through my clobber, checking out every little scrap of paper in my strides, even going as far as to ring any numbers she found.

Then she got religious. Now it's my reckoning that God goes out of his way to make things happen to believers just to give them something to pray about and Shelly was certainly spending a lot of time on her knees... and not so I could get on with doing my duty neither.

I didn't mind her sending the kids to Sunday school. At least it kept them from under my heels so I could curl up on the sofa and catch up on some kip. But when her fellow bible-bashers took to turning up at all sorts of odd hours, often talking about me well within earshot as if I was the Devil incarnate then I eventually cracked, we had the row to end all rows, and I packed my well worn old suitcase one more time.

It didn't take long for Trevor to move in and, to be honest, I wasn't even that upset about it. I knew she needed someone there; so did the kids and, in fairness, he was a decent enough bloke, even if crushingly boring, with a line in patter that was somewhat less exciting than watching paint dry. He was a bit of a born loser too.

Just consider this example of Trev's innate ability to come a cropper. He ran a van hire business, which would probably have gone under years earlier but for a regular contract from the local police who hired his vehicles when their own were off the road.

One day the plod turn up at his workshop and asked him: "Do you want the bad news or the bad news, Trev?

"You know that Transit we hired from you on

Wednesday? Well, I' m sorry but it was involved in a chase after some geezers who had knocked off a post office. They ran off the road, our driver couldn't miss them and the van we hired from you got written off, along with the getaway vehicle."

"Oh, fuck," said Trev, as one would. "So what's the rest of the bad news, then?"

"Well, sorry mate, but the van we were chasing was rented from you as well!"

THE LONDON TAXI DRIVER I PAID TO BASH ME UP

We were driving home after visiting Shelly's mum and dad to tell them we were breaking up. The old couple had recently moved to Basildon – I always thought Shell was an Essex girl at heart (question: what's the difference between Mr Gorbachov and an Essex girl? Answer: Mr Gorbachov knew the names of the 12 guys who screwed him when he went on holiday). We had just come out of the Rotherhithe Tunnel, heading south. I signaled to turn left as I was taking the first exit off the roundabout, planning to cut through to Peckham.

Already on the roundabout was a London black cab and he was taking the same exit as me, so I gave way, as you do, and then left the junction and ended up in the inside lane, driving alongside him.

The exit had two lanes and he was in the righthand one and I, in the left. But the cabbie ended up changing lanes without signalling. He seemed quite unaware I was even there, cutting me into the kerb in the process, so I sounded my horn to warn him so he would not run into the side of my car.

The berk swerved over the road and still ended up in the nearside lane (my lane) causing me to brake very hard – in fact I nearly put Shelly through the windscreen, which didn't exactly bring a smile to her face. Fortunately seat belts were being worn. However, I was naturally not too pleased.

Half-a-mile up the road I passed the cab driver and

shouted out, as one does: "You should learn how to drive mate." But not in those exact words! I overtook him and thought nothing more about the incident. About a mile up the road, I was sat at a set of red traffic lights and was waiting for them to turn green. Suddenly the cab came tearing along the inside and smashed straight into the side of my car, taking my nearside wing mirror right off. The cabbie pulled right across the front of my car blocking my path so I could not pull away, then jumped out his cab and came straight to the driver's side of the car.

Unfortunately, my window was open and he reached in and began repeatedly punching me in the head, then snatched my keys from the ignition and threw them across the road. I remember seeing that he had two passengers sitting in the back of the cab, looking really shocked. Then he jumped back in his cab and roared off in the general direction of away.

I was really shaken and Shelly dialled 999 on her mobile. Ten minutes later the police arrived and took all the details. I had to go to Rotherhithe Police Station where a full statement was taken. As I parked up outside the cop shop and got out my car I noticed the same taxi driver heading back towards the tunnel, aiming north. I went into the police station to make my statement, as I needed to get a crime reference number for insurance purposes. It tooksome time and as I was just signing the bottom of the form a copper came into the room and informed me that the taxi driver was at Tower Bridge Police Station at that very moment, making allegations that it was me who had assaulted him

I couldn't believe it. There I was, sitting in the interview room, shaken and certainly stirred, with red stuff all over my face and clothes – no, it wasn't ketchup: I'm not that messy an eater. Outside was my car, sporting a smashed wing mirror as additional witness to what had happened – yet the police were telling me there was not enough evidence for them to prosecute the cabbie for assault, even though he was sitting in Tower Bridge nick at that very moment with not even a scratch on him.

After visiting casualty at King's College Hospital to have my injuries looked at, I decided I would take civil action against the cabbie and represent myself in court, so I toddled down to Tower Bridge Magistrates Court next day and took two civil summonses out on him – one for assault and the other for damage with intent.

After a couple of months, the date for the hearing arrived. In the meantime, with Duncan's valued help, I had prepared all the necessary paper work. I had obtained copies of all the police statements, copies of my medical report and had taken a witness statement from Shelly.

I made several copies on the photocopier at the library and Trevor bound them in a neat folder for me. On the day of the hearing, I walked in the court and noticed my road-rage attacker talking to his solicitor. There was a bit of a reaction from them on seeing just me, a witness (Shelly) and no legal representation at all.

I walked in to Court Number Three to inform the clerk I was present and said I would be representing myself. I found this was quite an advantage, as I was given lots of leeway and was able to say exactly what I wanted, with very little restriction. I was given the seat where my legal representative would have sat had I appointed one, and conducted the case on my own. I circulated all the copies of evidence I had brought along to the clerk of court, the magistrate and the defence solicitor, who was a right smarmy bastard who kept trying to talk down to me, the public school twit.

The cab driver, who looked like he could go a few rounds with Mike Tyson, was then read the charges by the clerk and entered a plea of not guilty. I was given the opportunity to cross-examine him and was able to ask him a number of searching questions about the night of the incident. It was easy to catch him out on a number of items, as he had completely changed his story in court to the statement that he had originally given to the police. I was buzzing with it, I thought I was a right little Rumpole of the Old Bailey.

Just by referring to the original statements, I was able to

prove more than once to the magistrate that the cab driver was lying blatantly. I don't know why he had bothered with a solicitor because she didn't really get a chance to say anything of substance. It all seemed very cut and dried.

The case was found proven. The cabbie was convicted of the two offences and I was awarded £300 in compensation. This amount seemed ridiculously small, though, taking into account that I had taken a lot of time off work for the injuries I sustained – but I'd got a result.

To my amazement, the cabbie decided to appeal against the conviction and the case was then transferred to Knightsbridge Crown Court for them to deal with. On the day of that hearing, I submitted a medical certificate to the court explaining that I could not attend as I had undergone a minor operation that week, which was unrelated to the incident, and I wasn't feeling up to appearing in court.

I thought they would set a new date but two weeks later I received a curt letter from the court stating that the conviction had been quashed and I had to pay the cabbie's £250 legal costs. Knock me down with a feather – I could not believe it!

I did everything within my powers to have the case re-heard but the court officials told me that the matter was closed and there was nothing I could do to have it opened again.

This is one case I have never been able to get to the bottom of and until this day I don't understand what went wrong and why the verdict of the original hearing was overturned. After all, my evidence had been proven beyond all reasonable doubt. Yet the cabbie got off scot-free and I ended up footing the bill for his costs. It all seemed crooked to me.

The court harassed me for the dosh they had awarded him against me. However, I had been told that the cab driver would not receive the money until the award had been paid in full by me, so I decided to make him wait for it. I drip-fed money into the court a tenner or so at a time, waiting until they were about to send in the bailiffs before I sent each payment to them. I then applied to have the payments reduced to a pound a week, which strung it all out even more. It must have cost the courts more in time and trouble to keep chasing me up than they were collecting. All in all, it took four long years before I made the last installment but it rankles that, even if he had to wait, he got this money out of me – a fact which shows that sometimes crime does pay.

What's more, there was a nasty sting in the tail for me. Unfortunately, near the end of it all, I even let the one pound payments get a bit too much in arrears. I was out one day with my girlfriend of the moment, a real babe, doing some shopping. I decided that as we were near the court, I'd pop in and pay off the arrears of eight quid – two month's worth of payments – in one whack.

Unfortunately, because they felt I'd been taking the piss, they refused to accept payment and said I'd have to go in front of the magistrate as they'd already issued an arrest warrant against me.

An hour later, I found myself up in front of the beak who tore my head off and said: "This judgement goes back four years. You're down to paying a pound a week and you haven't even been keeping that up properly.

"You've got two choices, young man. Either you pay the entire remaining debt of £180 in cash, in full, right now, or I will send you down for seven days."

Bollocks, I had no cash on me, which I explained, so they held me in the court cells while my girlfriend went off to a cashpoint with my card and pin number to draw the money. It didn't help when the screw came to the hole in the wall – and I don't mean the cashpoint – and wound me up by saying with a leery grin: "Cor, mate, she'll be having a field day with your plastic. You won't see her back. They do it all the time."

I think this is the only case I have had to deal with where I became worse off as a result of taking legal action. And this is what they call fair justice!

However, I did eventually receive £1,000 from the Criminal Injuries Compensation Board for the injuries I had received.

Chalk it down to experience. I haven't got much advice to pass on about this one, except that you should never fail to attend a court hearing, even if you have to crawl there on your hands and knees through a field of broken glass. It's clearly obvious that overturning the original verdict was completely unfair to me but once it had happened it seemed I had no right to take my turn at appealing the revised decision.

From the first hearing, the one that I did attend, I came to understand something of how the more vulnerable victims among us feel, having to sit in front of their attackers in court. It is totally intimidating for the victim, although, because I'm a stroppy git and was determined not to let him get away with it, I didn't personally have any fear at all, despite the cabbie looking like a right hard nut. In fact I was enjoying it all like some great game.

Though I am learning all the time, I don't fully understand how the legal system works, but I do know that representing myself was not the problem here, and I totally enjoyed being my own solicitor. I do have a problem with the way the court's rules and regulations work though. Indeed, the whole system seems crazy and I often wonder if these magistrates and judges live on the same planet as the rest of us.

Surely they can't be as ignorant as they sometimes appear to the reality of everyday issues and the costs – both financial and emotional – which are involved for ordinary people who are, after all, simply looking for a little fairness?

Sometimes, however, justice does favour the little man. I have found the Small Claims Court to be a useful and inexpensive institution. You have to pay a fee, currently, £80, to institute a case, but you can represent yourself and, win or lose, each side is responsible for their own legal representation costs if they decide to involve solicitors, so you don't face the prospect of facing huge bills from the other side should you sue someone and lose.

Alan, an old schoolfriend of mine – one who did stay on and get his GCSEs, the bookworm – worked as a freelance magazine editor for a publishing company which suddenly decided to dispense with his services without giving any notice. Though Alan did not have a written contract, the small claims court arbitrator decided there was a verbal agreement, which is just as binding in law, and awarded him a month's money (£2,750), plus a day's lost income for attending the hearing, as well as travel expenses and the £80 court fee – and such results are final and binding, with appeal only allowable in the event of the arbitrator having broken some point of law in adjudging the dispute.

If you chose to represent yourself, as most people do, it is part of the arbitrator's job to take up any points of law on your behalf. So, unlike when representing yourself in open court, you will not get tripped up by your ignorance of legal jargon and the fine points in the way the system works.

An added advantage is that such cases are heard not in the forbidding environment of an open court but in the arbitrator's private office. The setting is informal, with very lax rules of evidence, making the whole thing more a discussion of the rights and wrongs of the issue than a confrontational battle of words bound by very strict rules of procedure and an overdose of legal jargon designed to bamboozle the ordinary citizen.

The disadvantage is that the case is heard in the home court of the defendant, which might mean the plaintiff – i.e you – having to travel a long way in order to get satisfaction.

In Alan's case, the other side – who had been arrogantly dismissive throughout and made a derisory offer of out-of-court settlement just the previous day – did not bother to attend the hearing but sent along a solicitor, who confessed in a whisper as they walked in to face the arbitrator: "I shouldn't be telling you this, but I don't think we'll be too long. They've given me no written evidence and no witnesses to call , so I haven't got a leg to stand on."

The small claims courts handle cases for up to £5,000 and are ideal for disputes with tradespeople, shops, slow paying customers and, especially, big faceless organisations, whether in the public or private sector. It might be someone who owes you money – be it a refund or the fee for some work you have done – or someone who has done you some quantifiable financial damage, like a neighbour who damagedf your property when putting up a new fence then refused to settle the bill for the damage. Use it, you'll like it.

" I SAY DRIVER, HURRY UP AND KILL HIM WILL YOU! THE METER'S STILL RUNNING!"

CONFRONTED WITH A KNIFE?: DON'T CALL THE POLICE

With my best friend, Mark, I had taken the cue from a brilliantly hot, sunny August day and driven down to the South Coast – with the Beach Boys' "Fun, Fun, Fun" blaring on the stereo – for an afternoon on the beach and an evening in leg-over city, scamming the always heaving clubs for talent.

Honest, guv, we hadn't had anything alcoholic to drink: I was on antibiotics at the time and don't drink much anyway, while Mark was doing the driving and, irresponsible though he is in most things – like remembering his old lady's birthday and paying his bills – he is meticulous when it comes to not drink-driving 'cause, needing to be mobile for his job, he can't afford to risk losing his licence.

Having for once failed miserably to pull, we left the last club on our crawl at about 2 am and were walking back to the car. We were cutting through the back streets as we had parked up near the local police station. If your car's not safe from tea leaves there, then where will it be? There was a convenient short-cut up an alleyway, which led us into the square.

As we came out of the alley I noticed a dosser pushing a shopping trolley with what looked like his home in it. I always feel an empathy for these people, whose problems are often not really of their own making, and I always buy a copy of The Big Issue.

I approached this bloke, who was probably in his early

twenties but looked a lot older with all that matted fuzz on his face, and offered him a fag, as you do. He seemed quite a friendly chap and was very talkative and sociable if not all that bright.

We'd been chatting for a short while when suddenly, out of nowhere, appeared a raving lunatic shouting: "Oi, leave my mate alone!"

This demented nutter was charging towards us in a frighteningly aggressive manner, brandishing a very large kitchen knife with a glistening chrome blade which would take pride of place in any Michelin-star chef's armoury.

Mark immediately shouted out: "Oh, shit, Martin, let's get out of here!"

Well, I certainly wasn't in favour of hanging about to exchange pleasantries, so we both legged it at a rapid rate of knots – unfortunately, in opposite directions, with me the one that the lunatic decided to chase after.

The only conclusion I have managed to come to is that this man must have thought we were giving his friend aggro – something which is too often suffered by down-and-outs on Britain's streets, thanks to all that vile crap they push out in The Daily Mail, The Sun and the other red-top tabloid rags about people on the social or living on the streets.

I'd run some distance up the road when I heard a lump of wood hit the pavement just behind me. I looked behind and saw that, having thrown this missile, my assailant had come to a stop, out of puff – so I just kept going for a while until I felt I was about to spew my ring and puke up a pavement pizza. Totally cream crackered, I waited on a street corner for some time to get my breath back – "I must start cutting down on the cancer sticks," flashed through my mind – before deciding that my would-be assailant had obviously given up the pursuit as a lost cause.

There was no sign of Mark, so I had no choice but to retrace my steps and try to find him. I cautiously walked back in the direction I had come from to see if I could find my friend and I started calling out his name.

I then reached the bit of wood, which was still laying in

the middle of the road, and decided to pick it up – after all it was a danger where it was, plus I could have used it to protect myself if the nutter should come charging at me again.

There's no way I would have attacked him if I saw him, but would simply rely on waving the lump of wood about in best ninja fashion to persuade the madman to back off. Frankly, I just wanted to get out of the place, retrieve the car and get off home.

I then heard Mark shouting out my name and we met up again. Mark said to me: "What was all that about? The geezer's a right bloody nutter."

Mark was clutching a red and white traffic cone. What he was going to do with that I don't know – I remember making a bit of a joke about it. We were both out of breath, wheezing like a pair of OAPs, and a little shaken – which is not surprisingly when you consider how we had suddenly been confronted with such a bizarre and very unpredictable and potentially dangerous a situation.

All sorts of weird things enter you mind at such times and, it might sound corny, but I really do remember thinking of my kids and how much I love them all.

We then started walking back towards where we had parked the car and I saw Mark leave the traffic cone behind, in the kerbside. As we reached the top of the road I noticed there was a large skip outside a shop where a lot of building work was being done, so I decided to lob the wood into this handy receptacle.

Just as the wood was arcing its way gracefully through the air on its short journey into the skip, two uniformed police officers came running around the corner. One of them grabbed me and the other seized Mark, and they then separated us. One of the officers took Mark off down the road a few yards. The copper was talking to him as they were walking and I saw them stop near a shop doorway.

The other rozzer started asking me about the wood and what I was doing with it, so I explained what had happened and told him about the man with the knife.

Well, this one was having none of it. He just grunted at me: "I don't think that's what been happening at all, do you? I'm nicking you for carrying an offensive weapon."

He had hold of my upper arm, quite tightly, and said: "You're coming with me, matey," and started force-marching me down the road at a pace the SAS would have been proud of matching. I also heard Mark protesting: "We ain't done anything! It was us being chased by a loony with a bleeding great knife."

The one who had me was walking me down the road so quickly I had to sort of run along with him, because he was a bloody giant compared to me and was taking enormous strides.

Before I knew it, I was hitting the deck with this great big lump of lard landing on top of me, screaming: "Get your hands behind your back!"

I then heard the footsteps of other police officers who were running down the road towards us shouting: "Do the bastard!" and they all just started putting the boot in, like a load of football thugs. I remember someone tap-dancing on my windpipe and someone else giving me a right hard kick in the small of my back. I tried my best to get my hands where they wanted me to put them but one was trapped by my stomach and the combined weight of the two officers who were piled on top of me.

When the handcuffs were eventually put on the coppers turned me over and one of these uniformed thugs stuck his big size-ten Doc Martin boot on my shoulder to keep me pinned to the floor. He then got on his personal radio and requested a van.

Mark was shouting: "Oi! What do you think you're doing? Leave him alone – we ain't done anything. There's no need for all that!"

Mark was then shoved into the shop doorway so he could no longer see what was going on. The van turned up and I was dragged up by the scruff of my neck and bundled into the vehicle, which already held two other prisoners and smelt of stale puke.

I had blood pouring down my face, my shirt – a Ben

Sherman, of course – was all ripped and I had the copper's foot print clearly marked on the back of it like the ultimate designer label. Naturally, I was very shocked and more than a little disorientated. After a few minutes, I noticed that Mark had been shoved in the back of the van too but he was up at the opposite end.

The thug (sorry, "The arresting officer") then sat opposite me with his whacking big boot, steel Blakeys and all, placed threateningly between my legs, as he muttered in a voice filled with venom: "I hope you're going to behave yourself, sunshine."

I remember Mark saying to me: "What have they done to your face?" I just sat quiet and didn't say anything.

Within minutes we had arrived at the nick, where we were taken to the charge room. I was asked to empty my pockets and then the custody sergeant asked the thug what I had been arrested for, to which my assailant replied: "Offensive weapon, assaulting a police officer and criminal damage Guv."

I immediately stood up and said: "What?!... where did that lot come from? I want to make a complaint against this man."

"No you don't – just sit down and shut up!" came the barked response from the desk sergeant.

The so-called 'offensive weapon' was the lump of wood, which certainly was not being used offensively; the 'criminal damage' amounted to the officer's watch strap having parted company with the watch, which had happened when they were jumping all over me; the 'assault on a police officer' was just one for luck, I think, because it was he who was carrying out the assault and I was the victim.

Mark was also arrested for having an offensive weapon – it's amazing the carnage you can wreak with a traffic cone! – and we were then placed in a cell. On the way I demanded to see the duty doctor as I was not feeling too good. It was two hours later before the quack visited me and checked me over. He recorded my injuries and advised me to go to the hospital as soon as I was released, so I could have an x-ray taken of my back, which he was a bit concerned about.

While banged up in the cell I had a visit from the thug who had arrested me. He came in, sat beside me and said in an altogether different tone: "I think you and your mate were in the wrong place at the wrong time. What we're going to do is take your fingerprints and some mug shots and then let you go. We're just going to give you a caution on this occasion."

He couldn't resist having another little pop at me though. I asked him: "Any chance of a fag?" and he handed me a Benson but when I said "Can I have a light then?" he sneered, "No, mate, that's dangerous. You might set light to the place."

An hour later we were taken back to the charge room and an inspector gave us a caution and released us. The implications of the caution were not explained to either of us. We were escorted out of the station and I remember the sergeant who showed us to the door telling me: "There was no need for what happened to you lads. If you've got any sense you should make a complaint – I would."

He must have known something I didn't about the character of the policemen involved but obviously wasn't going to elaborate. Mark drove me back to town, to his place in Nunhead. We had a cup of tea and then I got a cab to Kings College Hospital. I remember the sun was coming up at the time and it looked set to be a beautiful morning, which was ironic 'cause I felt like a sack of shit and the world seemed anything but a nice place to be.

I was examined, x-rayed and advised to rest. I had all my injuries recorded by photograph as well as their being noted on the doctor's record. I then made my way home, slept fitfully for a couple of hours and in the late morning I reported the incident at Dulwich Police Station. I got onto my pal Donald, who works as a gumshoe scribe on the local newspaper, and in the next issue they ran a picture of my battered boat race with an accompanying story, written by Don in appropriately lurid style.

The Police Complaints Department interviewed me

several days after the incident and this was followed up two months later with a curt letter stating that in their view there was insufficient evidence for any prosecution to be lodged against the police officers concerned. I then filed a civil action against the police for unlawful arrest, unlawful imprisonment, assault, and malicious prosecution.

All this happened near on a decade ago. We are now well into a brave new millennium, I'm older, wiser and a bit thinner on top and I am still fighting this case. I will obviously be seeing this through to the end, whatever it takes, because, as you know, "I ain't 'aving that!". The costs to date are unbelievably high – and we are talking thousands of pounds, part of which came, thank God, through legal aid – but I don't see why the very people who are supposed to protect us should instead attack us and get away with it.

"WATCH OUT, LADS, THE BASTARD'S GOT A TWIG!"

BLAME IT ALL ON GOD: BECAUSE THE INSURANCE COMPANY WILL

Of course, we all like to think we can put a little protection around ourselves by taking out insurance against the woes of daily life. But, wait a mo. Don't be lulled into a false sense of security. I had a personal injury and accident insurance policy and it was supposed to pay a weekly wage if I should be hospitalised for any reason.

Well, as far as I was concerned, I had been assaulted, albeit by the police, and I was legally entitled to make a claim under my policy. The insurance company, though, had other views.

I completed my claim form and duly sent it in to the company but a week later received a reply stating that as this claim was in relation to a criminal act on my part I would not be covered. I was shocked. If there had been a criminal act involved, it was by the policeman against me. It was like they were saying that as it was the police who had assaulted me it was my fault and I should just accept it.

It seemed as if I was being presumed guilty and that they were accepting the police version of events rather than mine. They were marking my actions down as having been criminal even though I had not been either charged or convicted of any offence and certainly denied that any such thing had taken place. I found this attitude of theirs to be very judgemental and I wasn't 'aving that, now was I.

I argued the point that just because it was the police who had assaulted me it didn't make such action on their part justified. Indeed, I made it clear to the claims people that I had already made a complaint against the police with the Police Complaints Authority and intended to take civil action against the boys in blue.

Accordingly, I felt I had every right to make this claim on my insurance. Due to the injuries I sustained I had to take quite a lot of time off work. I was admitted to hospital and had an epidermal injection for pain relief. I also had to undergo hydrotherapy and physiotherapy for about six months.

I was positive that the insurance company should pay me out, so I went through all the procedures and even went to their own internal complaints department. They were still quite adamant that they weren't going to pay me out and were trying to use all the get-out clauses they could find. In one letter I received they stated that the occurrence was an 'act of God' and therefore was not covered! I don't know where that definition of the work of the Good Lord appeared in the small print of the policy, or, for that matter, in the Bible, because I certainly couldn't find it – nor do I believe that God wears a dark blue uniform and acts like a thug!

They stalled me for months and months but I wasn't about to give in. Then their final decision was that there was no way they were going to pay out on this claim. So I took the matter to the insurance ombudsman, an independent body set up to deal with claims' discrepancies and disputes. I sent in copies of all the correspondence and proof of my completed claim form and asked them to see if they thought I had a claim or not.

After examining all the letters they felt that the insurance company should have paid out my claim. This took another three months or so to get sorted out, as the ombudsman had to justify the reasons for the decision. They then instructed the insurance company to pay me out.

While all this was going on, I had also notified my solicitors and they advised me that I was wasting my time pursuing this claim as they thought I would not get any joy, but I felt it was well worth taking the matter through to the bitter end. After all, I'd paid my premium and now I wanted the insurance company to honour its part of the deal.

I got there in the end, receiving two cheques, one for £806.67 and the other for £1,993.33

I was wholly convinced that I was entitled to this money and was also pleased that on this occasion I decided to ignore my solicitor's advice and see things through to a conclusion, even though my legal eagle thought I was wasting my time. I really didn't do any research on this case at all, I just thought that it should not make any difference whether I was assaulted by a private individual or a policeman; why should it? Just because they have a uniform it doesn't give 'em the right to go around thumping people, whether the person they attack is in the right or the wrong.

Insurance companies are very quick off the mark to take your money to insure yourself, your car or your house. They even write to you with enticing offers if your renewal is late. But when it's time to pay out someone on a claim they become very bashful and retiring. Far too often they'll give you a tremendous amount of stress in getting what is your due.

They will go to enormous lengths to avoid paying out a claim. They will, at times, even try to con you – and you end up being the one out of pocket.

Time was when insurance companies were in the business of selling us protection against the financial ill-effects of the misfortunes of life. Today, it seems they believe they are merely in the business of collecting premiums! When it comes to paying out claims they seem to believe that's somehow an unreasonable thing for the insured to expect of them. Indeed, they almost try to make you feel criminal for having the audacity to lodge a claim.

In the long run, they are only being fools to themselves with their greed. I know so many people who have had such bad experiences when it comes to making a claim –

being treated as a fraud suspect from the moment the claim goes in; being short-changed on valuations and so on – that they now only insure their car for third party rather than comprehensive and have let their household contents policies lapse. After all, why pay out all those whopping great premiums if, in the event of a claim, there's a pretty fair chance the insurance company will wriggle its way out of making payment?

What's that definition of an insurance company?: "Someone who offers you an umbrella when the sun is out, then withdraws it when it starts to rain."

Mark once had his car stolen. It was recovered but was in such a bad state that the insurance company decided to treat it as a write-off. Outside, the car was unblemished but inside it was trashed as a result of the thieves having ripped out the dashboard to get at the brand-new CD player and having liberally coated the interior with grease and muck while trying to remove the gearbox and gear lever. There were even boot prints all over the head-lining (I wonder what position in the Kama Sutra they might represent!).

The car – a black Ford Granada – was insured for the book price of £3,200. The insurance company – not a fly-by-night, cut-rate premium outfit but a pillar of the City – offered a paltry £1,800, notwithstanding that the car had been in immaculate condition, with regular service history, had five brand new tyres and that £900 CD system.

Mark wasn't 'aving that. He cut ads for identical cars from Exchange & Mart and sent them to the company with a letter saying: "I don't really want the money. Just replace the car with one that's exactly the same, like these advertised examples, which are even in the same colour."

The claims manager dug his heels in and refused to budge on the £1,800 offer. But that's when the insurance company made its big mistake. The argument had gone on for so long that policy renewal time rolled around.

Not only did the insurance company use the direct debit process to extract another year's insurance premium from Mark's bank account, for a car which they knew full well had by then gone to the breaker's yard and no longer existed, but they based the premium on an increased valuation of £3,500!

Not to put too fine a point on it, my pal had 'em by the nuts! A letter winged its way to the insurance company's chairman: "Unless I receive full satisfaction I will be reporting this matter not just to the Office of Fair Trading and the local trading standards people but to the police fraud squad as well.

"If they will not take action against you then I will institute a private prosecution for criminal fraud and I will hold you personally responsible as company chairman.

"You are either trying to cheat me out of my claim or you are trying to cheat me by charging me a premium which you know does not reflect what you yourselves believe to be the true value of my vehicle on which figure you would base any claims payment to me.

"You can't have it both ways and whichever way you look at it you are trying to defraud me. In any event, you know the car no longer exists so you are taking money under false pretences. I am sure you are aware that these are criminal offences for which you as chairman are responsible and which might well entail a prison sentence."

Needless to say, Mark got a cheque in full settlement, by return of post, and the amount paid even included a premium refund. What he didn't get, of course, was an apology.

PUBLIC HUMILIATION
BY THE BOYS IN BLUE

Run-ins with the Old Bill seem to be a regular punctuation mark in my usually rather humdrum existence. I had taken my four nippers out for the day, picking them up from their respective mums, Maggie and Shelly, and had driven them down to a nice country pub restaurant in deepest Sussex for a pleasant Sunday roast dinner – "Eat your peas you little toe-rags and Terry, stop pulling your sister's hair!"

We'd then gone to Box Hill to have a kick-around. Time was getting on, so I had to get them back home to their mothers, as I only had access on Sundays.

I took my two oldest children, Michelle and Tracy, home first as they lived in Warlingham. Then I dropped the other two, Terry and Sarah, off in Croydon, where their mum was taking them to the pictures. On the way back to my place I had to drive through Streatham, which is always busy on a Sunday afternoon.

As I approached a set of traffic lights that were on red, I dutifully came to a halt. Whilst sitting at the lights, I observed a large police van parked by the entrance to a block of flats adjacent to the lights. The van was packed full of coppers. I took very little notice of them, though they most of them seemed to be staring at me. The lights then changed to green and I pulled away. I noticed in my rear view mirror that the police van had pulled out and was now being driven immediately behind me, almost on my bumper, so I kept my eye on the speedo and made sure it didn't creep over the 30 mph speed limit. I did a left to get into the one-way system which would double back and take me up Leigham Court Road, towards West Norwood, and still the van followed.

Right outside the South London Press offices, the sirens began wailing and, in my rear-view mirror, I saw the blue lights flashing, so I pulled over as quickly as I could and came to a stop to let them pass. They then proceeded as though they were on a call – well, that's what I thought – but the van came to a sudden halt as soon as it was alongside me. The side door came sliding open and several burly policemen jumped out one after another, the first one shouting aggressively: "Get out of the car! Keep your hands in the air, don't touch anything"

I was highly confused and shocked that they were talking to me. I knew I hadn't done anything wrong, I hadn't committed any traffic offences and I knew for sure I wasn't on the run from some big robbery with sacks full of loot and marked 'swag' crammed into my boot.

I asked, innocently: "Do you mean me?"

"Out of the car. Now!" one of them bellowed back, so I did as I was told and walked towards the rear of my vehicle. It was like a bloody circus, they were shouting and screaming and passing members of the public, as always looking for some excitement to punctuate their otherwise mundane lives, were gathering to see what was going on.

One copper jumped in the driver's side of my car, another in the passenger side, one opened the tailgate and two stayed with me, pinning me against the vehicle, their faces inches from mine and rapid-firing questions at me.

At this point I was waiting for old what's his face, Jeremy Beadle, to pop out from behind a tree or something because their actions were like I had just held up the local Post Office with a shotgun yet I knew I'd just been out for the day with the kids. It had to be a giant wind-up.

It was a Sunday, it was 6:15 pm, it was very quiet and peaceful and it didn't really make much sense that they were treating me this way. I was in a right two and eight.

My car was a brand new and spotlessly clean Vauxhall Vectra, not some dodgy old banger. It belonged to the company I was working for and had nothing wrong with it physically as far as I was aware. So I asked the two officers, one being an incredibly butch WPC with what for all the world looked like designer stubble, why I had been stopped – but they just wouldn't tell me anything. I was only informed that they weren't happy with my car. I'm not sure what they meant by that exactly. It made me wonder if they didn't like the make of it, or was it just the colour that offended their sensitivities? – but the arse 'oles just wouldn't tell me.

I noticed one copper had gone to the boot, emptying all the contents out on to the pavement, while another two were searching through the door pockets and the glove compartment. Yet another had his head buried under the bonnet, perhaps he was looking for my secret forgery plant or whatever other dodgy thing they'd convinced themselves I was into.

One of the coppers with me started asking for my details: name, address and date of birth – you know the pack drill – all of which I quite happily gave. He was right 'arry dash, thought he was the bees knees, but had a right low melting point and started to lose his rag when I attempted to read him my bill or rights.

The WPC then asked if I had any identification on me, but as I reached in my pocket to produce what was requested I was pounced on by both of them and handcuffed. I was then accused of having an offensive weapon, you know, the one that didn't exist. I was then searched by the male officer and he removed my wallet from my back pocket. It contained Items like credit cards and a gym membership card with my photograph on it. I had other cards from work plus a bit of cash. I certainly never had an offensive weapon on me. Oh I forgot about the condom, maybe that was it?

The WPC then told me that I was drunk, so I invited her to breath test me as I was very confident that her findings would be very disappointing. I very rarely drink and if I do I will never have more than half a pint of lager top, especially if I know I am going to drive that day. And this time, I hadn't had a tipple in days. I was then told that my car was a ringer (a stolen car with a false Identity). Again I was very sure that it was no such thing because it been delivered to me brand new by Vauxhall themselves on a company lease so unless the guys up in Luton are a bunch of tea leaves there's no way the car was dodgy.

Then I was asked where my consignment of drugs was hidden in the car. It was a right Fred Karno's circus – they just kept going from one extreme to another with their ludicrous accusations. It seemed like they had my card marked and were determined to clear up their entire book of burglaries, and every other unsolved crime on the manor, against me. I was then escorted to their van, where the driver had remained all this time, and was told that I had to be strip-searched, as they believed I had drugs hidden on my body.

They bundled me, still handcuffed, into the back of the vehicle and I was unceremoniously undressed by two male coppers and still nothing was found, even when I did the traditional bend over and cough routine.

The door of the van remained open throughout the search and the windows were not even tinted, so anyone could look in and see me stark bollock naked – and I can assure you that ain't a pretty sight.

Eventually, I was released – with no charges made, no cautions given, no nothing, and with apologies notable for their absence. They never even asked me to produce my driving licence. I was absolutely livid about the whole ordeal, the way they had spoken to me and the manner in which they treated me. Their conduct was rude, aggressive, absolutely unprofessional and wholly unacceptable. They didn't give a monkey's about my rights or how I felt.

I went straight down to the local police station, which was in Streatham High Road, and made a formal complaint against the officers I had suffered the misfortune of bumping into.

I requested to see the duty inspector, as he's the one who has to take the complaint. When I made mine it was a sergeant who took the details, as he was acting inspector (playing at big boys eh?). He tried for about two hours to talk me in to leaving the whole matter in their hands but I was adamant that I wanted my details to be logged as an official complaint and insisted that this matter to be investigated.

Two weeks later I heard from the complaints department. They wanted to arrange an interview. An appointment was set up and an interview was arranged at my solicitor's office. A very detailed statement was taken which ran out to a closely-typed nine-page document. The interviewing officer then revealed that I had been stopped because I had a wonky numberplate on the rear of my car!

I was dumbfounded: this was first I had heard of exactly why I had been pulled over. The officer then produced a document called a 'search record', which is a form that must be completed if a policeman carries out a search. It contains pertinent information like the officer's name and number, the location and the reason for the search. That's when I found out that it was the Territorial Support Group – ie, the people charged with rooting out terrorists like the IRA – who had stopped me.

My copy of the search record makes interesting reading. It states that I was handcuffed because I kept trying to put my hands in my pocket, and that I was searched because my jumper smelt of cannabis!

I then heard from the Sun newspaper and they arranged for a photographer to visit my home to take some pictures. The headline of the resultant article blared: "COPS STRIPPED ME NAKED AS CROWD WATCH IN STREET".

Thanks to Donald, the story was also covered by the South London Press. If it had been a weekday, he would have been right on the spot to witness the whole thing as it happened but filling him with three pints at the Crown and Greyhound in the village was enough for him to get the gist of it all.

Three months later, having heard nothing, I contacted the police complaints people but they said they were still investigating the matter. They also told me that they were intending to make some house-to-house enquiries and planned to take some photos of the scene, though I could not see much point in this, especially as there are just shops and offices in that part of the street and, being a Sunday when the incident happened, they had all been shut at the time. The witnesses had just been passers-by who would be very hard to trace.

Quite frankly, I feel that this was all being done far too late. Even if they could locate any witnesses, who's going to remember reliably what had happened so long ago? Perhaps that's why they left it so long, maybe they didn't want anyone to remember what had gone down.

They also told me that they were having trouble identifying all the officers involved – and that is what I didn't really understand as there were names and numbers plainly stated on the search record. In any event, they must have had a record of who was working that shift and was in the van at the time.

A year later I received a reply from the PCA. It stated there was insufficient evidence and all allegations were denied. In fact, the whole report was a load of rubbish and very contradictory. One of the officers conducting the complaint even ended up collaborating with one of the officers involved and trying to cover things up. He stated that when I was interviewed about my complaint he noticed that my car numberplate was wonky. But my Solicitor and I had been out and looked at the car with him and there was nothing abnormal about it whatsoever.

I reckon the whole process of the Police Complaints Authority stinks and is a total waste of taxpayers' money. The police investigating the police – that really makes sense, now doesn't it? You somehow know what the outcome is going to be before it's finished, don't you?! It stands to reason that the ranks will close and they'll stick up for their own.

Well, I ain't 'aving that, so I haven't given up on this one yet and will now pursue this in the civil courts in due course; well I have got six years in which to take action, so the case continues.

It may be of interest to know that any member of the

public can quite easily obtain a copy of 'P.A.C.E', which is the "Police and Criminal Evidence Act" , available from any HMSO bookshop. It is a very informative document that outlines the guidelines which the police are meant to abide by, although, by my reckoning it is rare that they do it by the book anyway.

This publication is supposed to be readily available at all police stations for members of the public to view, especially if they should have the misfortune of being in custody at the time. I have put this to the test on a few occasions (not while banged up, I hasten to add) and the police didn't really want me to view it. They kept me waiting over half an hour at Peckham police station once and, when I finally did see the document, a police officer remained present in the interview room with me whilst I looked up what I wanted to know. I really got the impression that they didn't want me to see it, so the next day I went and bought a copy of my own. It joined my ever growing and well-thumbed legal library.

IN THEIR CLUTCHES

Remember the 'I'm Backing Britain', 'Buy British' and 'British Is Best' campaigns – all posters, stickers and Union Jack flags? What a load of cobblers. Once the hallmark of quality, 'Made In Britain' has long since become synonymous with 'cheap and nasty' or, in many cases, 'bloody expensive and nasty' – hence my long-standing practice of favouring Japanese cars (my current Vauxhall Vectra love affair excepted), much to the disgust of my grandad, who had served time as a prisoner of war in Changhi Jail under the Japanese and thought that any nation that subsisted on boiled rice and raw fish was not to be trusted.

Toyota, Mitsubishi, Mazda – I've owned 'em all, usually bought secondhand and with at least five and sometimes six figures on the mileometer, and I had always found them reliable and cheap to run and maintain. I used to reckon that even if you took all four wheels off they'd still keep going. Until, that is, the infamous clutch saga.

My endless succession of jobs had rolled on as I fought to earn enough to pay all that maintenance money the two mums were trying to squeeze out of me so hard that even the Queen's face on the notes was looking pinched (have you noticed that acid-look Liz gives as she stares out from a tenner?).

I became a qualified driving Instructor and my latest set of Japanese wheels was a neat little Nissan Micra. I purchased it new and was paying for it on tick. It was cheap to run and seemed a pretty reliable motor but after about a year the clutch started slipping, so I thought I'd better get it looked at.

I would have taken it to Uncle Alf but we'd had a falling out over a dodgy motor he'd sold one of me mates. That's the trouble with Alf. He's a decent enough bloke when you get down to it; got a heart of gold really, but he can't resist the temptation of using that silver tongue of his to stitch people up when it comes to business. He'll always use that old "Business is business, my son" excuse, but that doesn't wash with me. I reckon you should treat people with the same respect where exchange of money for business is involved as you do in private matters – especially if they are mates.

Anyways, I went to three different places, including a Nissan main dealer, to get quotes for the work. They were all talking telephone numbers, of course.

Bob's yer uncle, I eventually, found a branch of a well-known so-called clutch specialist, which was conveniently local. I told them what was happening and they gave me what seemed a reasonable quote, certainly better than anything else I'd been offered and within what I could afford. So I booked the car in for the replacement – which they said would cost me about £98, including fitting. I collected the car that same evening and paid the bill. Within three days the clutch felt like one out of a fucking big lorry – it was very hard to press the pedal to the floor, unless you happened to be wearing lead boots at the time.

I took the car back to the clutch centre and they made a few adjustments and it was fine for another two days – then the bleeding thing started getting stiffer than a vicar's dick again. I duly returned to the garage and the geezer said it was a faulty clutch unit – "It 'appens sometimes mate. It's just one of them things" – and said they would change it for another one.

The car was fine for about three weeks but clutch number-two started giving me grief as well. I called the garage and they said to take it back, no probs. So I did. They made more adjustments and played about with it for a bit. I went back a few more times but it never really got any better, so I got on the phone to head office and had a right old whinge – you know the routine.

Later, while on a driving lesson, the gear change became very stiff and the gears couldn't be selected at all – which was most embarrassing as I had a learner driver behind the wheel at the time, We were stuck mid-way round the busy Beckenham roundabout, the one by the cinema, and the silly mare started freeking out. I called the garage once more, feeling more than a little miffed, and they arranged for a breakdown truck to come and collect us.

By this time it was getting beyond a joke. I had to keep cancelling lessons and was consequently losing a lot of money, along with my reputation for reliability – and that really got to me because as a rule you can set your watch by my comings and goings. Not only that, but I had a neat little sideline going in dipping my wick where some of the better looking lady pupils were concerned, but having the clutch go on you rates on a level with running out of petrol. These middleclass suburban housewives might enjoy their bit of nooky on the side but they want to be double sure of getting back 'ome indoors long before the old man appears for his tea.

The next day I collected the car and it had a further replacement – clutch number-three was now in place, or so I was told.

The car was fine for about a month, then one day, on another driving lesson, the clutch started smelling really bad. My student must have thought I had a terrible wind problem and kept letting them off, which wasn't helping my cause any, since I knew she was gagging for a good seeing to after three lessons worth of playing that old hard-to-get routine and I really thought I was on a promise.

The clutch had totally burnt out. This time I called the AA recovery service and they took me back to the clutch centre to be booked in yet again. They had the car for another two days and then fitted clutch number-four but, believe it or not, that too soon started playing up. This was now becoming beyond the mere ridiculous.

I was in a right two and eight. I had no choice but to go

back to the same place, as I had already paid them in full. It stands to reason, I felt that they were obligated to get it put right. I was now becoming their worst nightmare and they mine. They even had to involve their area manager after some insistence on my part. He assured me that the car would be A1 double ok next time I collected it.

The geezer that I had previously dealt with had disappeared from the scene. When I questioned his whereabouts they told me he had left the company. Can't say I'm surprised – I'd been making his life hell and he was always in a tizz, sweating away and looking like he was on the point of keeling over with a dicky ticker.

Two days after I collected the car, with clutch number-five in place. I was on a lesson with a student in the Crystal Palace area. The lass was quite confident and was soon due to take her test. She'd even agreed to go out for a drink with me to celebrate the ritual burning of her L-plates. I recall we were practicing hill starts off Auckland Road. Just as she was ready to move away at the bottom of a rather steep gradient on Fox Hill we heard this very loud bang from under the bonnet and the car came to an immediate stop. The poor girl thought she had broken it. I got out of the car after pulling the bonnet catch but couldn't see anything wrong: everything under the lid looked absolutely normal.

Then I peered beneath the vehicle and saw my gearbox sitting forlornly on the road in a slowly spreading shallow grave of oil and clutch fluid! Yes, the whole gearbox had come away from the engine. I telephoned the clutch centre and they arranged for the car to be taken back to their workshop… yet again.

After I had left the workshop and got a cab home, borrowing a fiver from Jenny for the purpose, I telephoned other clutch centres and just picked their brains for advice. Of course, just like builders, who always criticise each other's work, not that they would do it any better themselves, they loved telling me horror stories about the company in whose care I had placed my car. In the process I gathered quite a bit of knowledge about the deeper mysteries of car clutches.

One of the garages advised me to get the car inspected by an engineer who specialised in problems of this nature. After many calls, the name of Mr Ivan Hill kept coming up. It seems he was a respected consultant and technical author working in the automobile industry: a man who really knew his nuts and bolts, so I got in touch with him. We arranged a surprise visit to the garage first thing the following morning. He was the best.

We went in and Ivan asked for the manager. My man then showed some identification and demanded to inspect his client's (me, that is) car. The vehicle was put on a ramp then raised six feet in the air so he could have a good gander underneath. At this point he noticed that the gearbox was not in the car or even in the workshop. He asked where it was and to our astonishment they said they didn't know!

Ivan, who was quite a comic and knew just how to be sarcastic, could not believe what he was hearing: "What do you mean you don't know? Surely you must know where you've put it? It's a bit big to be lost," he said pointedly.

The manager's reply couldn't have been more vague: "Head Office have sent it away to be repaired, but I don't know where. I think it will be back in the morning but who knows?"

Ivan asked many other searching questions and then we left the workshop. We returned the following day. On close inspection, Ivan found a number of things wrong that were of a very serious nature and, so he said, negligence had a great part to play. The core of the matter was that the replacements had been carried out by a lardy apprentice who really didn't know his arse from his elbow. Each time he'd worked on the car he'd made a right bodge of it. He'd cross-threaded things and even sheared off a couple of critical bolts, so no wonder none of the clutches had functioned properly.

We then gave the clutch centre boss a list of demands and a time limit to have the car sorted out. A week later I received Ivan's detailed report, on which I would later be relying in court. I then went round to see Duncan at the library and he helped me to start legal proceedings against the company for negligence.

I had 'em bang to rights. My eventual reward was an out-of-court settlement of £3,000 for all the aggravation, plus legal costs of about £500, the price of the clutch (£99) and finally the cost of Mr Hill's report.

From start to finish this case took from late 1989 through to1994 before they agreed and finally coughed up. That's nearly five wearisome years – but it was worth pursuing.

I think that the lesson to be learned here is that you must know a little about consumer rights. In this situation, I was relying on the professional skills of the fitters to make a proper diagnosis and carry out the repair correctly. I knew that having asked for the work to be done, I had every right to expect it to be carried out in a satisfactory manner.

Just talking to other garages which specialised in the same type of work was very beneficial. Not surprisingly, I found that rival companies absolutely loved slagging one another off and generally putting each other down. However, cutting through the sour grapes and crap and getting right to the chase, my knowledge of car repairs increased enormously, to the point where I could speak almost as an expert and certainly run rings around anyone trying to bullshit me.

Coming across a man like Mr Hill was a stroke of good fortune and proved the most beneficial element of all. When you want to fight the system, expert witnesses of this kind count for a lot, especially if the case goes as far as court. Remember, a lot of the toss-pots you will come up against really only have limited knowledge and experience in their supposed field. Many of them are in the job they are doing only because they can't get anything else. They don't care and they don't learn. If you let them, they'll try to bamboozle you with a lot of technical stuff and nonsense but an expert in the field can cut right through their crap and get straight to the crux of the issue.

THE SHOP THAT FREEZED MY FRAME

There was a time when shops could be relied on for expert advice but these days you'll be lucky if the person who serves you knows as much about the product as you do yourself. What's that old saying?: "Pay peanuts and you'll get monkeys".

I needed to buy a video recorder. Normal routine: I shopped around for the best price and after deciding what make and model I wanted, I bought a Toshiba Nicam digital stereo from a well-known high street chain that claims to pride itself on good value and good service to go with it – but don 't they all? (no names, no pack drill – I don't want the bleeders to sue, now do I?).

This piece of kit cost me £525 and came with the normal 12 months guarantee that you would expect with a new purchase.

Anyway, two days outside the guarantee period the machine started to play up. Typical isn't it? The problem was that I was getting terrible interference when I recorded in Nicam stereo.

I took the machine to an authorised repairer, a place which belonged to the chain I originally purchased the machine from. It was in their workshop for about a week. I got the bill, paid it and took the recorder back home. I set it up again and did a bit of recording but the fault still remained.

I returned to the repairer and they had it fixed again under their three-month repair guarantee. It was in the workshop for a further three weeks whilst parts was ordered. I then received a telephone call to come and collect it. I took it home, set it up again and it was fine. I fully tested it and everything seemed hunky dory. Or was it? Within a month the fault re-occurred. I again contacted the repairers and this time they said they would visit my home. They were under the impression that I had set it all up incorrectly. It's just my luck for things to go wrong on me and then have the toe-rags try to say it's my fault.

The engineer came round and, miracle of miracles, turned up exactly when they said he would. He fully checked the video and re-tuned my television. He had the video in bits for two hours and came to the conclusion that my aerial was the cause of the fault. I found this hard to believe, as it had been okay for the previous year. It seemed to me that, unable to find the real root of the problem, he was clutching in the air for porkies to fob me off with.

He told me that I needed a special aerial that could pick up Nicam signals and recording would then be much more effective and the sound quality would improve dramatically.

I called the local aerial installers and paid for a special Nicam aerial to be installed. It cost £140, only for me to find out that the fault still remained. I was furious. Well, as we all know, I wasn't 'aving none of it.

I went straight down to the repair shop on the button at 9 am the next morning and took the matter up with the manager. Believe me, he was totally embarrassed. My main concern for the moment was to get the machine working but I knew I would be taking up other matters with their head office at a later stage.

The machine was taken in again for a further three weeks and I was told that I wouldn't get it back until they were happy it was working as it should be, which seemed fair enough. More parts were ordered and fitted and I then got it back. It was fine for about four months until the fault re-occurred, but this time it wasn't within the repair guarantee period.

It was fixed again and had new heads fitted this time

and I got another bill, this time for around £95, which I reluctantly paid. It occurred to me that by this time just about every component had been replaced but the case! I just wanted my video back in good working condition because I was missing all of my favourite soaps. When I got home the machine was exactly the same, with no improvement whatsoever. So this time I took it to the top, the very top. I contacted the company's head office that very day and spoke direct to the managing director.

I told him the whole sorry story, making sure to keep cool and not lose my temper but being firm at the same time, and I made a few demands. I also suggested that they let Toshiba repair it as I now had very little faith in their in-house engineers.

The next day a courier company collected the video recorder from my home and took it straight to Toshiba's head office. A week later Toshiba called me and said the machine was beyond economical repair. They told me I would have to take the matter up with the shop directly, so I did. They also arranged for the video recorder to be replaced with a brand new machine, which was promptly delivered to my home.

By being persistent, I finally got the shop to cover the full cost of the replacement, which was the latest model at the time. I was also given a scart lead with brass connections to improve recording quality and a full refund of the entire repair costs. As well as the normal 12-months manufacturer's warranty, I got an extended 12- months parts and labour guarantee.

I find that when dealing with any repair type problem, things never seem to go straightforwardly. You send for the engineer to have your washing machine repaired and they have to come back two or three times before the job is completed. You have the T.V engineer round and he has to come back later to finish the job. I again refer to consumer rights as enshrined in the law of the land. If a repair is carried out it should have some form of warranty on the work that is done – and it is best to have this clarified before having the job undertaken.

It is also advisable to log down every phone call made, the time and date and who you spoke to. Always find out what position they hold within their company; then if the problem needs to be chased further through the system you know who you have spoken to already and who you haven't. It has now become customary for me to go straight to the top at the first smell of trouble with any problem that has to be sorted.

These days, of course, with automated phone systems, it is difficult to actually get through to speak to anyone. After having spent two solid mornings trying to get through to the service department at AEG, a friend of mine sent a fax direct to the company chairman. It read: "Is there life still at AEG, or are you the Marie Celeste of the washing machine business?" The result was an immediate phone call from the head honcho's secretary and the problem was dealt with immediately.

In my situation with the Nicam machine I felt I was well within my rights to insist on having this unit exchanged for a new one. They had carried out loads of repairs unsatisfactorily and had the machine for a total of four months (if all the days were added together). It was also fair to demand a full refund of all the parts and labour charges involved in the abortive repairs, as it was obvious that all the parts I was charged for and the work that had been done had been a waste of time. I was a victim of their incompetence and, as you know by now "I ain't 'aving that".

STOKING UP PROBLEMS

I decided that I wanted a nice fireplace to be the centrepiece in my front room. I shopped around and I haggled a bit, as you do. The starting price was £2,200 – this was the first quote I got. After phoning round several shops, I managed to get a quote as low as 700 notes for the same thing, but without the trendy logos on the box.

I had this way located exactly the fireplace that I wanted at a price I was willing to pay, in a well-known major DIY store I thought could be relied on. I had carried out all of the research needed to make sure it fitted my needs and that I could get it installed without problems. However, choosing what you want to buy is just the starting point – getting it supplied and fitted can be quite another matter.

When I was ready to buy it I went to my local store, ready and eager to place my order but they never had the item in stock. I rang a number of branches until I found one that had all of the parts that I needed (the store concerned was 15 miles away). I asked them to reserve it for me.

The offer included the marble surround, the base unit and the fire itself. I advised them that I would be coming down to the store at the end of the day to collect it. I also asked them to check and make sure that there were no parts missing, as I wanted everything to run smoothly on installation.

I hired a van and went to collect the fireplace but when I got there I found that three of the parts had not even been reserved for me, despite my having been assured on the phone that they would be. I just saw two boxes labelled with my name and another label with check marks on it. I didn't believe they had actually been checked by the shop because one of the boxes still had the manufacturer's cable ties around it and these would have had to have been cut to get into the box. I went away with the two boxes marked A and B. These boxes contained just the fire itself, in a two-part kit.

I had a whinge at the manager and created a little fuss just to show them I was not taking any crap from them. After all, I'd travelled a long way. I then insisted that he locate all the other parts that I needed and had ordered. After 20 minutes he had tracked them down at – would you believe it? – my local branch. He then told me that they would be ready for collection on the following Monday.

Once again, I hired the van and went to my local branch to collect the bits but when I got there nobody knew what the fuck I was talking about. I got hold of the manager to sort it out. He then arranged for another branch to deliver the missing bits to my house. I went home and rang the company's head office and chewed their heads off. I just love driving everyone mad: you get quicker results that way as they can't wait to get you off their case. I called on the hour, every hour to see what progress was being made and insisted I spoke to the same person each time I belled them.

Meanwhile, I had arranged for a builder to come and install the fireplace. After haggling over the price for his work, we booked a date and he turned up promptly at eight on the arranged morning. He started knocking holes in walls, pulling up floorboards and so on, until, wait for it, his work ground to a halt because half the bloody bits were missing from the box.

Would you adam and eve it? – there were no instruction manuals for installation or for operating the fire. I needed the diagrams and specifications for the hole in the wall. This was a special type of fire you see, for use if you didn't already have a fireplace in the house.

I called head office and asked for customer service. Firstly, they contacted the manufacturer who then faxed a copy of the instructions to the local branch and I had to go and collect them. They gave me 30 pages of thermal paper that was all curled up and very informative: I think not!

All the wiring diagrams were in black and white and so fuzzy as to be near unreadable, so they were about as much help as a chocolate fireguard would have been for the fireplace once installed.

After telephoning the store and going mental, I then rang the manufacturer and explained what had happened. They said they would put the originals in the post. I tried to make the best of what was faxed to me. I first ticked off the checklist with all of the parts and then discovered that a number of the bits needed were still missing.

I got straight on to customer services again. Their solution was that they would locate all of the parts that were missing and send them to me in the post in two weeks' time. I wasn't 'aving that so I then rang the managing director of the company and insisted he should locate the parts and have them sent round by taxi. I must have made an impression on him because, apparently, eight branch managers became involved in locating all of the missing items. I had a number of phone calls that day from various of these bods in a vain attempt to verify what was still missing against the parts they had located for me.

Threatening to ring up BBC's Watchdog consumer protection programme, I also said that I'd be taking the company to the Small Claims Court. Whilst all this was going on I was having a hassle with the builder because he was telling me he would not be able to finish in time unless the gear turned up pretty soon. I only had a week I could take off of work, my house was looking like a bombsite, and to add insult to injury, the builder was on a day rate for standing around with his hands in his pockets.

The builder said he was fully booked up for the next three months and would not be able to return till after that – great, since he had already started knocking holes in the wall. He was leaving me right in the shit. I know it wasn't his fault but it was not mine either.

Within five hours all the parts were taxied around to me so it meant that I could start installation the next day. I ended up finishing the job myself. I then decided to telephone the managing director again. Surprise, surprise, he would not talk to me but within ten minutes I had a call from the manager of one of the stores to talk about the problems I had suffered. After a 45-minute conversation, with me explaining how incompetent their staff were, we then negotiated compensation.

At the end of it all, they sent me £150 by way of a cheque plus a £30 gift voucher to spend in the store. Their opening offer had been a mere £60!

This well-known store's management had proved to be totally incompetent and they hadn't fulfilled their obligation as a supplier. They had clearly made serious errors and caused me great inconvenience and expense, so there was no way I was going to end up out of pocket. I will say that they did sort things out reasonably quickly once the problem had been addressed and I felt their offer of compensation was almost fair.

BODGE, SCARPER & CO

Of course, if shops are bad, things can be much worse when dealing with builders – especially those of the jobbing variety.

Warning bells should have rung when I noticed the chunk bitten out of his ear, leaving a perfect set of teeth marks.

He was the sort who knocks on your door to ask if you want the drive re-surfaced with Tarmac: "We've been working on the motorway, guvnor, and have got some gear left over – we can let you have it for a good price, so we can. Cash only, of course."

You rise to the bait of a seeming bargain, forgetting that there isn't a motorway within miles. Once hooked, the nightmare begins.

In my case, the itinerant tinker had noticed the dire state of my front garden: "We'll dig that crazy paving up for you in no time, Sir, and put down any surface you want," he assured me earnestly in a rich Kerry brogue.

I was a bit strapped for cash but it was a job which had wanted doing for some time and I had the feeling the neighbours were beginning to talk about the eyesore which was blighting a street where house prices were rapidly going through the roof. When I'd moved in, the neighbourhood had been full of beaten-up old Sierras with no tax discs. Now there was a fair sprinkling of new Mercs and even a couple of Porsches. We were being gentrified.

So, after a bit of haggling, I fell for the trap: "Dig it up, get rid of the rubbish and re-surface it with some nice shingle," I said. "Oh, and don't forget to put a membrane down first so the weeds will not grow back through."

"Fair enough, Sir," he replied, in that charmingly lilting voice.

"I'm a bit strapped for cash at the moment, so don't do the work yet. Come back in a couple of weeks and I'll let you know when you can start," I instructed.

It was just a couple of days later when my mobile rang. It was my current girlfriend, in a panic: "Mart, there's a couple of strange men in your front garden smashing up the paving."

I would have rushed straight back but I was at the tricky point in negotiating a deal which could earn me some handy readies. I got home that night to find the job completed. It looked fine. I had my suspicions, however, and started to brush away some of the gravel. I only had to go down an inch or so and there it was – solid earth, and no sign of a plastic membrane. It rained most of the next day, and the day after, and by the weekend the weeds were already starting to spring up through the gravel.

Your man was back on Sunday morning for his agreed £200: "A nice job, don't you think, Sir? Oh, and me and the lads would like that cash you owe use, if you don't mind."

"But what about the membrane you were supposed to put down first?" I enquired, "The job's useless without one – I'll be inundated with weeds. They are already coming through."

He looked incredulous: "And what might a membrane be, guvnor?" he asked.

"The thing you agreed you were going to put down before you laid the gravel!" I snapped back.

"Oh, no, Sir! You don't want something like that, you need to let the gravel breathe."

There were remarks thrown at me about his knowing some heavy people but I stood my ground. Reluctantly, Paddy and his oppo went off, acquired some thick plastic sheeting from I know not where, dug out the gravel and re-laid it on top of the sheeting.

The coverage was minimal and it was obvious half a

dozen sacks more would be needed but by now I just wanted to be rid of Bodge, Scarper & Company so when they said they needed some cash to buy the extra gravel I paid them their 200 notes in full. They said they'd be back in half an hour but, of course, and as I expected, I never saw them again – which was something I was quite happy about until my next door neighbour returned from holiday a week later and came thumping on my front door.

He was livid: "Your workmen have dumped all your rubbish over my garden fence." He fumed, " My plants are covered with dirt and chunks of broken concrete," he further complained in a brook no nonsense voice which said unspoken: "I want it shifted and I want it shifted now!"

Building scams are legion. The do-as-you-likey-pikeys will offer to check your guttering and clear it of debris, return down the ladder with a dead squirrel they've planted in their bucket and convince you that the guttering is rusted away, you've got loose tiles on the roof and that your loft is infested with vermin – which, of course, they will remove... for a healthy fee.

The lesson is obvious: never let anyone convince you that you need work doing. Get a second opinion from a registered builder or qualified surveyor. Remember, by and large you get what you pay for in this life. If someone offers to do work on a ridiculously cheap basis then they've obviously either nicked the materials or will bodge the job with sub-standard gear and poor workmanship. Instead of saving dough, you will like as not end up having to pay twice before you've got the result you want.

TILL DEATH US DO PART

Thankfully, some of the things that go wrong in life happen without us ever knowing about them and, as they say, what you don't know about can't hurt you.

Just consider the simple matter of dying, for instance – and it's something that happens to all of us eventually.

A girlfriend was returning home from the crematorium with her father's ashes in an urn when she tripped and fell. The lid came off the container and her dear departed did, well, just that – the wind swirling him off to the four corners of the earth.

Of course, she could have gone straight round to her mum's and confessed the truth but that would only have caused misery to her family, who would probably never have forgiven her clumsiness. So, instead, she rushed home to the barbie, scooped out some ash and re-filled the urn, which now enjoys a hallowed place on her mother's front room sideboard.

Things often go wrong at funerals without the family knowing. A chauffeur friend whose black stretch-limousine sometimes does service as a hearse recalls an occasion when he and four of his mates solemnly unloaded a cheapo coffin only to drop it off their shoulders. In horror, they saw the lid spring open as the box collapsed and watched the dead body roll out!

Alan swears that stiffs sometimes get mixed up and that, in the case of cremation, there's no guarantee of ending up with the right ashes – but if you don't know, then who cares?

Illusion is what matters most in modern life. We buy the packaging rather than the contents – if it was otherwise, nobody would ever purchase a McDonald's!

Just take the limo business for instance. Most people haven't got a clue when it comes to cars. Put personalised plates on a Jaguar – and if you don't care what number you have, you can do this for as little as £250 – and it's only real motoring enthusiasts who know the car isn't a new one.

I had a friend who used to impress American clients by sending a smart black Jag to pick them up from the airport. The driver – a retired chauffeur who did the job for a couple of drinks – would get his uniform out of mothballs, there'd be a ten quid bouquet of flowers on the back window ledge for the missus and a bottle of malt Scotch for the Yank himself. The car itself was 15 years old and worth no more than £800.

The whole exercise cost my pal less than £50 a time but he swore it was worth an extra nought on the bill he'd slip to the oh-so-impressed client.

I once played driver myself. I had an old but rather immaculate black Ford Granada Ghia. Alan phoned me in a panic. He was a car short for a big function; would I like to be a chauffeur for the night?

We had to pick some big-wigs up from an embassy in Kensington and drive them to the first night of a musical at the Aldwych Theatre, hang around while they watched the show then had their supper at the Waldorf Hotel next door and then drive them back to their homes in West London. It seemed like a pretty easy way of earning a quick one-and-'alf cash-in-hand, so I was well up for it.

The only trouble was that the traffic on the night was atrocious, my thermostat jammed and the car began to overheat. Now, as anyone who spends their driving time at the wheel of an old banger will tell you, the time-honoured get-you-home remedy in such circumstances is to wop the heater up to maximum and switch the fan to full-blast.

In the rear-view mirror, I could see the beads of sweat start to appear on my passengers' brows. All I could do was sneakily wind all the windows down and pray nobody would notice the little whisps of steam which were starting to waft out of the bonnet.

Fact is, the journey would have been far more comfortable by bus, but the illusion was that they were going to the theatre in style, so who cared?

The other drivers and myself spent most of the evening in the Soup Kitchen, swapping yarns, and the clients were so pleased with their stylish mode of transport that they gave us all tickets for the following Saturday's showing of the musical.

It was lucky we went that night because the show closed the following week, the victim of terrible reviews. The critics had a field day, slating everything about it. Yet on the night we went the cast took four curtain calls – quite an achievement considering the show was playing to a theatre which was much less than half full.

The truth was, it was a good show – strong storyline, some memorable songs, brilliant staging and fine performances. Had it been written by the ghastly Andrew Lloyd Webber it would doubtless have been a West End smash and gone on to conquer Broadway too.

So what went wrong? Well, the fact that the show was financially backed by an obscure Pacific island built of guano – that's bird shit to you – gave the critics an irresistible opportunity to vent their spleen on an enterprise which really did deserve to be better treated.

It was the Polynesian diplomats that we had taken to the opening night. In recent years their island had turned into a goldmine – well, actually, a shit mine, as the Aussies excavated the guano for its phosphate content (great for fertiliser). The island's economy had been transformed. Suddenly everyone there had become silly money rich. Trouble was, though, that like all natural resources, the source of their good fortune was rapidly running out. It was as part of a move to diversify that the island elders had invested in the show. Had they done so in secret all might have been well, but unfortunately they'd laid themselves wide open by publicising their involvement and consequently they'd lost their Hawaiian shirts on the venture.

As I said, it not the content that counts most but the packaging you wrap it up in.

DON'T WHINGE: COMPLAIN!

The way we Brits like to moan, it's no wonder that the Aussie's call us "whingeing poms". On the other hand, we don't like complaining.

What's the difference? Well, moaning is when you go on and on and on to your family and friends; complaining is when you take things up with the people who have actually been winding you up – like council officials, parking wardens, waiters, manufacturers.

If you've got a gripe, it's best to take it up with those who can actually do something about it – even if, at first, they shrug their shoulders and say there's nothing that can be done.

Working late, years ago, we sent the office boy out to buy some meat pies and hot tea. The pies were so stale, so rock hard, that when one of my workmates smashed his against the edge of a desk some chips of wood splintered off! We all moaned and groaned but didn't bother to do anything about it.

But one of the lads didn't let it rest. He sent the offending pie back to the manufacturers with a letter which read something along the lines of: "Dear Sirs, I suggest you are in the wrong business. You should sell your pies as tombstones – they would certainly withstand the ravages of weather and time."

Such studied sarcasm can often bring results. In this case, the manufacturers not only refunded the purchase price but, by way of apology, sent along a massive hamper filled with their products.

Don't be rude, offensive or downright insulting: that will ensure you'll simply rub them up the wrong way and rather than getting action will find yourself encountering the proverbial brick wall. However, a touch of barbed witticism will usually help to get a result.

When I was a young lad, someone in our cycling club gave me a couple of unused 26-inch Dunlop tyres which had been languishing, covered with dust and pigeon shit, in his loft. As my wheels were 27-inch, I fixed the tyres to a branch of my dad's cherry tree then hung two buckets of hardened cement from them. They stretched a treat, fitting perfectly, and I got two years of good wear out of them before, bang, bang, they both blew out within a couple of days of each other.

Incensed as only a stroppy 14-year old can be, I sent them back to the manufacturers with a suitably sarcastic letter. I got as good as I gave. To their credit, the complaints department sent me a voucher for 75 per cent off a new set of tyres but along with it came a masterpiece of a letter: "Dear Mr Rogers," it read, "We thoroughly agree that you had a right to expect longer life from these tyres and therefore hope you will accept the enclosed voucher in recompense. However, we would point out that they were manufactured very many years ago – in 1956, to be precise and are now a discontinued line."

Complaints departments are, of course, your first port of call but if you don't get satisfaction from them then, as I've already advised, don't be afraid of taking things right the way to the top, making sure that you keep a note of who you spoke to along the way and what was said as your complaint progressed.

Of course, you are likely to find the complaints department excruciatingly hard to contact: I hate to think how many CDs worth of wallpaper music I've listened to while being kept on hold.

You've probably noticed how very much easier it is to get through to the sales department. Well, if that's the case, lay the problem at their door and insist they do all the running around for you. Get a name and always ask for the same person whenever you call. Eventually, they'll become so fed up that they'll be moved to do something about the problem, if only to get you off their backs.

When dealing with the retail or service industries remember that, at the end of the day, they want your money. Major hotel chains have developed the habit of asking you to leave an imprint of your credit card when checking in, just in case you run up bills for room service, telephone, mini-bar or whatever, then do a bunk without settling up.

But if they can't trust you, why should you trust them? What's to stop them billing you with things you haven't had – charges which you will not discover until you get your credit card statement months later when you are back home on the other side of the world.

My answer is to simply say "Sorry, I don't use credit cards". Now that really throws them. They then ask for a cash deposit, to which I respond: "No, just take the mini-bar out of the room and block off the phone."

In my experience they prefer to forget about a deposit, give you the key and let you get on with it, taking the chance that you'll be honest rather than losing your custom for sure. Provided you look half-decent and don't come across as simply being a stroppy git, they'd prefer to take a chance on you than to risk having a room go empty.

It's rather sad how little trust there is in the world today and I personally find it offensive to be made to feel as if I'm automatically regarded as a potential criminal. If bank clerks and shop assistants are going to hold my £20 notes up to the light to see if they are forged then I'm going to do the same with any notes they give me in my change. They really don't like this but logic says they are just as likely to pass a dud to me as I am to pass one on to them.

I'm afraid banks simply can't be trusted. They make mistakes, big time – and it's the devil's own job to get them to own up and put things right. When you open an account you are effectively giving the bank an open cheque book which they can dip their greasy mitts into any time they want.

Banks are amazing places. Try paying cash into a business account and you'll find charges appearing on your account for a transaction which is, effectively, one where you are lending them your money! I wish I could get them to pay me for borrowing their money.

Of course, the reason why private individuals and small businesses get the rough end of the pineapple is because the big multinationals have such negotiating power that they end up virtually paying no bank charges at all.

Well, if the big boys can negotiate preferential deals you owe it to yourself to try to do the same for yourself. It's amazing how many hotels will give you a discount on the published room rate (or rack rate as it is known in the industry), if only you have the balls to ask for it while giving the distinct impression that failing a reduction then you'll turn on your heels, walk out the door and look elsewhere. This especially applies in the late afternoon or early evening when they are panicking about having rooms left empty, whereas later in the evening they are likely to call your bluff, knowing you will be the one worrying about ending up with nowhere to sleep. It's all a bit of a game, but one that's worth playing if it works out to your benefit.

Shops too are often susceptible to barter. The philosophy is simple to grasp: it's better to sell at a reduced price than see a potential customer walk out of the door empty-handed.

My father-in-law went into a shop in Walworth Road after spotting some trousers he liked in the window. He tried them on but they didn't fit properly.

"We can alter them for you for a small charge of £5," said the shop assistant, adding with a pleasant smile "and we will have them ready for you on Saturday."

The response was immediate and pointed: "Why should I have to pay extra and be made to wait? I'm sorry I can find another pair of trousers down the road that will fit and I can have them now."

Shelly and I cringed but old Charlie was right and not only did they carry out the alterations within half-an-hour and waive the £5 charge but allowed themselves to be brow-beaten into giving a discount at the same time.

SHOP-LIFTING MALARKEY

It's one matter being caught bang to rights but there are few things worse in this world than being accused of something you haven't done – especially if you are a young and vulnerable teenager. I gave my two older girls 25 quid each to go and get some new clothes, as I wanted them to look the biz when I took them to meet my new girlfriend. Michelle was 14, so she was old enough to look after her 12-year old sister.

Off they went by bus to the local shopping centre for a spend-up, went to the American Embassy, sorry, McDonald's treated themselves to a Big Mac and a Coke each and then headed straight for a well-known chain-store whose clothes were very much in-vogue with youngsters like them (whoever invented branding was a clever bastard and definitely an anti-Christ as far as the harassed parents of this relentlessly consumerist world are concerned).

Like typical women, the girls fussed their way through various items, trying several of them on before Michelle at long last found a blouse she really liked.

She took it across to the till. The cashier offered her a carrier but, as her purchase was a small item, Michelle decided to put it straight into her own bag, which was stronger than a plastic one since it was made of leather – well, a good imitation of cow skin anyway! – and it had the advantage of having a shoulder strap.

As the girls made for the exit, they were accosted by a tall, spotty geek of about 22, with razor-cropped hair, a single earring and an ill-fitting dark-blue suit, who, in an unnecessarily loud and dramatic voice, announced himself as the store detective and accused them of shoplifting.

"I saw you put something into your bag you little tea-leaf," he hissed.

"I know you did," replied Michelle, shaking with a mix of embarrassment and fright, "But I've paid for it and I've got a receipt."

"Don't give me that crap, we've had enough of people like you," the Neanderthal proclaimed, grabbing her forcibly by the arm and marching her off to the manager's office with her now tearful and terrified little sister in tow.

Once there, they were confronted by a severe, school-marm looking woman in her forties or fifties, with thick-framed glasses, a face like a slapped arse and her hair tied in a bun, like one of those Russian spies in a James Bond flick.

The old cow started threatening to call the police and went on and on about how it was company policy to prosecute any shoplifters, by which time both girls were scared shitless.

Michelle's bag was grabbed off her shoulder and the contents unceremoniously dumped on the manager's desk and rummaged through. A smile of sadistic delight spread over the store manager's face when the blouse tumbled out, though it was quickly followed by the receipt – yes, evidence from their own store that the item had been paid for.

But instead of a red-faced apology and some immediate offer of compensation for having wrongly accused the girls, the dastardly duo – Shit For Brains and Ms Grumbling Tit-Mould – treated them to a long lecture on the evils of shoplifting and the intense lengths the store's management were going to in order to stamp it out. And the girls were even told not to come back and shop there again.

What a fucking liberty! First off they detain two kids and humiliate them in front of a store full of people and then when they find the goods have been legitimately bought and paid for they give 'em a long-winded ear-bending and leave them feeling like they are criminals anyway. What a way to instil a sense of right and wrong in a couple of youngsters.

Now, like me, my kids might have a good eye for a bargain, but they've been brought up proper, with a strong sense of right and wrong. They wouldn't buy hookey gear off the back of a lorry and they wouldn't so much as nick a handful of sweets out of Woolies.

What's more, if the till girl had insisted on them taking the blouse in one of the store's carrier bags in the first place then the whole incident would never have happened.

Needless to say, the girls forgot about the rest of their shopping and headed home after their ordeal, just in time to interrupt the Saturday sports on the telly – and I had a tenner riding on the 3.30 at Newmarket. They were badly upset by the whole affair and little Tracy was still shaking with fright. They told me the entire story and I was straight on the blower to the store, with, you'll not be surprised to hear, the thought "I ain't 'aving that" uppermost on my mind.

I got really pissed off when I asked for the manager and, instead of putting me through, the muppet who answered the phone started questioning me about who I was and what I wanted. I really hate that and always feel like saying: "I'm me, you plank, and what I want to speak to your boss about is none of your effing business."

After having a right pop at the manager, I demanded her name and the phone number of her head office. I rang them and insisted, forcefully, on speaking to the managing director. Go straight to the bod at the top is a solid principle in circumstances like this.

Boy, did I express my feelings over the way in which my daughters had been treated. I was careful not to be abusive or overly aggressive and threatening but I got in a few powerful digs and made it clear that if anything like it ever happened again I would sue the store for wrongful arrest and unlawful detention and go for substantial damages.

Well, I think the geezer was convinced that I meant business and he said he would investigate. True to his word, he got back to me within the week, offered his profound apologies and sent us a £100 voucher to spend in any of the company's stores, along with a letter saying that company procedure was being revised as they didn't want something like this to happen again.

I have to say, he handled it well and managed to turn a very disgruntled person into someone who will now tell people that his stores aren't that bad.

That's one of the oldest but least appreciated lessons in dealing with people who have a gripe. Apologise profusely and make amends to someone you've wronged, even if you don't think you were anywhere near as bad as they reckon you were (let's face it, most complainers go right over the top), and you will win a friend for life, turning a negative event into a positive result.

Just think on this. You go to a restaurant and the food is good and the service excellent. You've enjoyed it but you may never get round to going back and you quite likely will not tell anyone else about how good a time you had.

However, you go somewhere else where the food is naff and the service slow. You complain, the manager offers you a couple of double brandies, tears up the bill and patiently explains that his chef is off sick and half his waiters did not show up for work, and your whole attitude changes.

Instead of feeling narked you actually feel a bit guilty about having complained. Though you will almost certainly never go back – after all, it's been one of the worst nights out you have ever had – you will probably end up telling other people what a nice restaurant it is!

I can give you a real-life example of how the principle works. A friend of mine, Tony, was a brilliant restaurant operator in terms of getting punters through the door and, just as importantly, attracting them back time after time.

He had a great memory and took orders without using a pad, but the minute he got out back in the kitchen he'd write up a card for each customer, which he'd keep in a card index system. On the card he'd write down the food and wine which had been ordered.

Next time the customer came he'd impress them by

saying something like: "Did you enjoy that bottle of Sancerre you had last time?". Once a pattern emerged he would be able to change that to: "A bottle of your usual, sir?" and make the guest feel like they were someone really special.

He did it for me once. He knew I liked a particular sauce, made from Calvados apple brandy and cream, which happens to go equally well with a nice pink breast of Donald Duck or a thick slice of porker.

On this particular evening I had a new bird on my arm, a right cracker I was out to impress – roger me rigid, why else would I pay Tony's extortionate prices?

Anyway, the chicken dish on offer that night came with a peppercorn-based sauce. But when I ordered it, Tony asked me with a flourish: "Would you like it as it comes, Sir, or would you care for your special sauce instead?"

Boy was the bird impressed, she thought I must be some right important toff to get such special treatment. Her knickers were already as good as in my pocket! It was no big deal for Tony, though. All he had to do was put the sauce laddle in that pot over there instead of this one right here.

On another occasion, when I was a bit flush after a good tickle down the dog track the previous day, I went to Tony's gaff for lunch – he did a good-value set menu. I wanted a blow-out and to catch up on what was going on around the manor (Tony always has his ear to the ground). As I was finishing off my coffee, in walked a couple of, well, latter-day hippy new-age traveller types. You know the sort: beads, earrings, hair down to the waist – and that was just the bloke!

They were right scruffbags of the kind you wouldn't expect to find in a place where most people would wear a suit and tie or a new frock, depending on what sex they happened to be, of course – though, these days, perhaps they'd cross-dress!

Anyway, I was the only other customer in the place, so Tony let them in and offered them the menu, though he confessed to me later that he was wondering whether they had the dosh to pay the bill or, indeed, if they might be a couple of animal rights protesters who'd suddenly stage a sit-in. The second of these worries evaporated when they decided they were going to order a mighty expensive couple of lobsters – but that only heightened the worry that they might not be able to come up with the dosh at the end of the meal.

When it came to the vino, they plonked – well that's probably the wrong word, 'cause it certainly isn't plonk – for a very expensive bottle of red Bordeaux, a Pomerol, at 60 sovs and nothing off for bringing the empty bottle back afterwards. Intrigued, Tony asked them if they were out celebrating. A birthday, perhaps? Or maybe an anniversary?

"No," came the reply, "We've both just lost our jobs and we aren't likely to be able to treat ourselves to much more than pie and mash in the future, so we decided to push the boat out and have one last fling on the redundancy money."

In short, they were following the time-honoured "The condemned man ate a hearty meal" principle.

Tony was so impressed by their happily fatalistic attitude that he insisted on breaking out a very nice bottle of Bollinger Champagne so we could all drink a toast to "better days" before our brave duo slipped off into the nether world of UB40s, dole queues and Marmite on toast.

"Don't judge a book by looking at its cover" is an old saying which we should all adopt far more often. Others would say: "You are what you wear" but why should it be so? – and, in any case, the rules of the game are so often perverse.

Now, you won't often find me tarted up in a monkey suit but I did once get invited to a big black-tie society 'do' held in a swish nightclub in Soho. My mate Simon had pulled some posh totty in Stringfellow's a couple of nights earlier and she'd wangled him a couple of tickets. So I sloped off down to Moss Bros, in Covent Garden, one afternoon and rented a tux, dicky-bow, the works. All dolled up, I looked the biz.

Simon is a diamond geezer but lives in a bit of a fantasy

world. He can carry it off, though. To be honest – which he never is! – he's got more front than Buckingham Palace.

To Simon, life's a breeze. A crisis is when he's down to his last four Armani suits, somebody has walked off with his Penthouse magazine and he can't find the corkscrew. He's done alright for himself, in a modest sort of way. He's had a couple of dodgy deals turn into nice little earners, invested in some property, brought some bodgers in to do it up on the cheap, sold it quick, to get a nice little turn on his dosh, and has never looked back – though he's often caught taking a peek sideways.

Everyone seems to think he's a real face, king of the manor, big kid on the block; truth is, though, Simon's as often brassic as he is flash with cash – but he never lets on that's he's got his back to the wall and if everyone thinks he's a big wheel he's not about to tell anyone he isn't, now is he?

When I first knew him at school, Simon had the arse hanging out of his trousers and couldn't afford The Beano. Nowadays he drives a Jag, a tasty-looking XJ6, and comes across all flash. Ok, so the motor's 10 years old and barely worth the grand he gave my Uncle Alf for it, but he keeps it spotless and he spent 150 knicker on a personalised number plate, so now it's only people who know their motors who realise it's not a new car.

I remember going up west with him one time. He stuck it on a double yellow, left it unlocked, with all the windows and the sunroof open and his mobile sitting on the front seat. Off we trotted and had lunch, did some shopping, cut the breeze with some mates we ran into, and didn't get back to the car for a couple of hours.

You've guessed it, when we returned to the car it hadn't been ticketed, let alone clamped or towed away. Nor had anyone reached in and nicked anything. And, despite the ever darkening skies, it hadn't rained on his leatherwork. He's that kind of guy – born lucky. Mind you, I couldn't imagine him getting away with that sort of stroke these days when they'll have your eyes out and sold before you've even had time to blink.

He lives in a flat in Dolphin Square too. It's a great address to have; never mind that he's just looking after the drum for a Saudi pal who's never in the country; that the phone's been cut off, and that most weeks he hasn't got a pot to piss in, Simon's got the image of success hanging over him. He's got the flash wheels, lives in a great flat and does all his business on the mobile so why should he care if it's all a big sham? And if the birds fall for it, so much the better.

Anyway, Simon arranged for me to meet him in the residents' bar at Dolphin Square, which is, or was, the largest apartment block in Europe, set right on the river near the Tate Gallery. I felt a bit conspicuous sitting on the 185 bus from Camberwell in full evening dress like a right tit, but I couldn't afford a cab, so what the hell?

I arrived early and, walking into the bar, caught sight of myself in a mirror as I entered. If I say it myself, I looked more suave than Roger Moore himself and decided I'd elbow me way to the bar, fake the accent and order a vodka martini "shaken and not stirred" of course. But, as I did so, I felt a tug at my coat-tail and looked down to see a little old lady, holding a menu. "Excuse me, young man, can we order now?" she enquired, assuming that, dressed as I was I must be a waiter. It didn't do much for my ego, I can tell you!

I was back on top when we got to the function, though, slurping Champers with all the 'Hurray Henrys' and their Sloanie bints, watching out not to drop me aitches, acting like a right Jack the Lad. I even tried a couple of oysters but downing them resembled sucking snot off an ashtray. Give me a plate of jellied eels any day!

Later that evening, walking back through the depths of Soho towards Leicester Square in the vain hope of getting the last Northern Line tube south – Simon having minced off with Fiona in hope of a bunk-up – it occurred to me that the people I walked past would not think I was some sophisticate who'd been drinking Champers and mixing it with celebs all night, but a bouncer on his way home from duty at some sleazy strip club.

Another time, Simon asked me to do a favour and drop something off to him at the Dorchester, where he was meeting his Saudi mate for lunch – no prizes for guessing who was gonna pick up the tab.

When I arrived, Ahmed insisted I join them for the posh scoff. Now, if I say it meself, I wasn't togged out bad. I had a neat pair of strides on, a Pierre Cardin shirt that mum has given me as a Chrissy present, and a beautiful Aquascutum kid-leather jacket which cost 600 notes off the back of a lorry, and no change for a cappuccino.

I only got as far as the Grill Room door when some snotty head waiter stopped me and said: "Sorry, Sir, you'll need a jacket and tie or I can't admit you."

Feeling somewhat put down by this, I was all ready to slope off and settle for a fry-up at the nearest greasy spoon caff instead, but Ahmed piped up: "He's with me, and I insist you serve us."

Now, with all the dosh his kith and kin spend there, they weren't about to argue the toss with the boyo – but rules is rules, so they conjured up a jacket and tie for me to wear. Never mind that the neck-strangler had soup stains on it and that the jacket was a red wine-waiter's issue that was two sizes too small – I was now up to par regulations wise and deemed good enough to eat their over-priced fodder.

It brought to mind the joke related by black American comedian Franklyn Ajaye, which I retell something like this: "I've made the big time since last I played here, so I booked myself into the penthouse suite at the best hotel in town and decided I'd splash out with a meal at their gourmet French restaurant, which has more stars than an Academy Awards Oscar's presentation.

"I put on my silk shirt, my $5,000 Versace jacket, my alligator skin shoes, my gold chains and Omega watch and waltzed up to the restaurant door.

"The head waiter put his hand on my chest and hissed: 'I am sorry Sir, I cannot serve you unless you are wearing a tie'.

"I looked him straight in the eye and replied: 'Look,

Man, my jacket cost more than you earn in a month, my shoes could buy your grandmother and you can kiss my arse… '

"To which he responded: 'I am sorry Sir, I cannot kiss your arse unless you are wearing a tie!"

How you decide what you should wear when going out to eat is one of those great mysteries of being British. It's like you can go into a working men's caff for your bacon, sausage, egg and bubble and know instinctively that you should leave a 50 p tip on the table when you leave, yet go to another caff the next morning and know that if you left a tip in that gaff they'd think you were being a right flash 'arry.

There are posh drums where everyone wears trendy gear and you'd feel a right plonker if you turned up wearing a collar and tie and others, which might well be less expensive, where exactly the opposite applies and formal rules ok – collar, tie and jacket are a must. How do you tell one from the other? Fuck knows! But somehow you know instinctively before you even step through the door. I suppose it just comes with the territory of being British.

Of course, it's all a load of cobblers. What's more, the rules don't apply to everyone – could you imagine Tory, sorry, Tony Blair being turned away because he's wearing an open-neck shirt? Or Liz Hurley being ejected for wearing a dress cut too low?

It's not just hearsay; I can give you solid evidence. One of my many jobs was as a bouncer – sorry, meet-and-greeter – at a swish dine-and-dance night spot in a posh outer suburb (another time I got to wear a Dicky Bow!). It wasn't quite in black tie territory as far as the guests were concerned, but not far off it: the sort of place the likes of you and I only get to go to for our daughter's engagement celebration or our golden jubilee.

Simon was messing about in the video production business at the time and I had this idea that the club would make a great place for shoots, so I talked to my governor who agreed that I should invite Simon and his current piece of fluff down for the evening, to have a meal and suss the place out.

So far so good, but Simon belled me the night before to ask if it would be ok for them to bring a couple of big-knob friends from Canada with them.

Again, I cleared it with the manager and everything seemed hunky-dory, until they turned up. Simon and his lady were fine, but their guests!!!…

She was wearing a black cut-away vest over a skin-tight leopard-skin leotard and had the biggest pair of Bristols you've ever set your eyes on – with nipples that stuck out like coat hooks. Her false finger nails, painted lurid pink, with a diamond embedded in each one, were long enough to enable her to scratch her arse by reaching over her left shoulder. Her lipstick shone like a stop light and her false eyelashes could shelter you from a rainstorm, while her hair was bright ginger with purple highlights and was such a mass there might well have been exotic birds nesting in there somewhere.

As for the guy, he had the most amazing tan and was built like a brick shithouse but with a skinny waist and nine-inch hips. He was wearing skin-tight black leather strides, held up with a two-inch studded belt with a brass buckle big enough to sink the Titanic.

His pecs showed through the skin-tight black vest and his biceps strained against copper amulets while his wavy blond-on-blond hair tumbled to his waist in vast billows.

"Fuck it, there goes my gig," was my first thought. Having invited them, I couldn't very well turn them away, now could I? – besides, if I'd tried, the guy would probably have beat the crap out of me and had my liver for breakfast, with some fava beans and a nice Chianti, but they were breaking every dress code in the guvnor's book.

I was in a blind panic. I got the head waiter to put us at the table no right-minded punter ever asked for, as it was tucked away almost under the staircase that led up to the Champagne bar.

It was then that I spotted the club's bank manager and his wife, sitting with one of the owners, who I knew was trying to raise some extra dosh to extend the place.

One thought crossed my mind. Yes, you've got it in one: "Oh, bollocks!"

Then it happened. The bank manager spotted us. He took a double take then stood up and walked over to us, a pen and a piece of paper clutched in his hand, and went straight up to the blond Adonis: "Can I have your autograph for my daughter, please?" he asked.

Turned out, my unexpected guest happened to be the lead singer in a Canadian heavy metal band whose number-one fan just happened to be our bank manager's nearest-and-dearest offspring.

It's funny how life takes such bizarre twists and turns. From wanting to hide the guy away, out of sight, suddenly the spotlight was on us and I was a hero for having brought such a superstar into the place! Thank fuck nobody sussed out that his partner happened to be editor of one of the world's leading porno mags – or maybe, for all I cocoa, she was the bank manager's own secret heroine.

LITTLE THINGS MEAN A LOT

As I've already whittered on, if you go to a restaurant and have a magical meal, there's nothing to say you'll ever go back again. If, on the other hand, it's a disaster but the manager handles the problem the right way you'll end up recommending the place to your friends.

Why then do more businesses not realise that a complaint presents a golden opportunity to build a strong and profitable relationship, provided you treat the customer with both courtesy and generosity. Soup cold? Don't charge for it. Booking messed up? Find them a table somewhere else, pay for the cab to get them there and invite them to come back another night for a complimentary meal. The dividends of such good PR can be enormous.

After I quit my gofer job, well, actually I got sacked because I'd fucked off down to the coast one day with one of the typists and they found out, I worked for a short while in the stores at a major record company which had a policy – even back then when customers' rights were far less well guaranteed in law – of no-quibbles replacement of faulty goods.

A doctor wrote to complain that his copy of Beethoven's Fifth Symphony skipped when it got to a particular rather strident piece of the music. Why anyone would want to listen to that racket anyhow is beyond me, but to each his own. Anyway, I sent a replacement by return, with a suitable apology, only to receive an even more irate letter. A second replacement met the same response so I tried the returned disc on my record player in the office: nothing wrong, it played perfectly.

I naturally suspected something was faulty with his equipment – maybe he simply needed to invest in a new stylus! – and wrote suggesting the geezer check for this possibility. An even angrier letter landed on my desk: his hi-fi was new, state of the art and there was nothing at all wrong with it.

Rather than saying, "Sorry, there's nothing more to be done", and simply refunding his money but still leaving the man disgruntled, I asked him to let us know what make and model of sound system he was using and then got the people at the factory to try our version of Beethoven's Fifth on exactly the same kit. Low and behold, they got the same result – it skipped. Investigation showed that by some quirk or other that particular recording and that particular hi-fi were incompatible, the modulations being enough to skip the needle out of the groove.

Instead of just sending a copy of the report and a refund, I wrote a letter along the lines of: "Dear Sir, I regret that you will not be able to play our recording on your stereo. Knowing how disappointed you must be, please accept the six classical recordings enclosed, with our compliments, and select a further six of your choice from the enclosed catalogue. These will then be sent to you without charge."

I didn't hear anything for weeks, then through the post came the catalogue, with not only the doctor's six choices marked but a list of 50 others – plus a cheque to cover their cost. It turned out that he'd been so impressed with how we had handled his complaint that he had been enthusing about us to his patients and friends and had not only taken orders from them but had collected the money too!

So it was that an extremely disgruntled customer was turned into our best salesman – and we didn't have to pay him any commission, let alone a salary!

The ability to turn disasters into triumphs is one of the keys to successful business. Attention to the smallest details is another. After all, it's the little things which really matter the most.

Picture the scenario. Shelly and I, back in the days when we were still getting it on, were staying at a smashing little country pub in Berkshire. Everything was perfect – except that the bed creaked seriously when Shelly was in action, but, then, she could bring a slab of concrete to orgasm if she wanted. Dinner was wonderful, even if we didn't understand half of what was written on the menu, when suddenly water started dripping through the ceiling and onto our desert plates, splish, splash...

We rush up to our room. It's flooded, water is running down the walls. It turns out one of the occupants of the staff flat above our heads has dashed down late to start work, forgetting that she has left the bath running.

We ended up mucking in, helping clear up the mess and assuring the embarrassed owner that there was nothing to worry about – even though our suitcases were bobbing round the room doing a fair impression of the Spanish Armada and it took a day to dry and iron all our clothes. It was that time-honoured 'Dunkirk Spirit' in action.

Not only did we not moan but we ended up firm friends with the owners and went back several times. But just imagine how different it would have been had we found there was no bog paper in the kazee, if our wake-up call hadn't happened or if the steaks we had ordered well done had arrived oozing blood? It's the little, not the big things that truly irritate.

At the end of the day, we all realise that everyone's human, that things do go wrong and that none of us is perfect. It's how things are put right that makes all the difference.

Just before the railways were privatised, I was travelling to Glasgow to visit my mate Gordon and his missus. It made sense to take the InterCity night sleeper out of Euston. I went straight to bed and had a good night's sleep, waking up at 8 am in what I assumed was Glasgow Central Station, only to find that the sign read: "Milton Keynes". Oh, shit!

It turned out there had been a major storm in the night and someone's garden shed had been blown onto the railway, bringing down the power lines. I couldn't resist asking the steward: "Was it the wrong kind of garden shed?". To their credit, BR broke out the bar, gave everyone free food and drinks and made me a full refund on the ticket price.

Less than a month later I was travelling back down from Newcastle on the East Coast line after helping Mark flog off some disco gear. We'd left Tyneside at 3 pm and should have been back in London for early evening but once again the weather blew up. Eventually we ground to a halt on an embankment somewhere in the wilds of Northamptonshire. It was so windy that even though the train was no longer moving forward it was swaying so much from side to side with each gust that people were actually feeling seasick!

Fuck me, it could have been like waiting for the Titanic to go down, but the crew were right on the button. A mobile phone was handed round so that passengers could phone home to worried families, the buffet car was thrown open and snacks, drinks – even bottles of wine from the restaurant – were handed out free of charge, and not just to the toffs in first-class.

And when the food ran out? Well, eventually, over the fields came a little man weighed down with two wicker baskets full of sandwiches and other snacks. Sorted.

When power was restored, we finally limped on into Kings Cross, where we arrived at 3 am, and there to meet us was a fleet of cabs – supplied free, with the compliments of InterCity, to make sure everyone could get home ok, including the couple who needed to be in Ashford, down in deepest Kent.

What's more, everyone got a full ticket refund. Evidently some seven trains had been caught up, with around 200 people on each, so the total cost of all this to the railway was colossal. It was, however, the cheapest PR they could have bought. Everyone went away waxing lyrically about how well InterCity had handled the affair and I'm sure that next time anyone of us overheard someone bitching about British Rail in some pub they would immediately have jumped to the railways' defence.

As I've said, it's all a matter of how it is handled. Lockerbie was not in any way Pan Am's fault but the way the yanks mishandled everything was the final nail in their corporate coffin. They came across as arrogant, uncaring and more interested in covering their own arses than looking after the victims' families.

On the other hand, being a matter of pilot error, the Kegworth M1 air crash at around the same time could be laid firmly at the door of British Midland. However, the company handled it all so well. Sir Michael Bishop and his fellow directors were not only on the scene within minutes, handing out the hot, sweet tea and sympathy but made no attempt to try to make excuses. As a result, the company image got a tremendous boost, to such a degree that their flight bookings in the following months actually rocketed upwards rather than plunging down.

LIFE ON THE MOVE

My 'ol mum reckons it never hurts to be nice to people. I received an object lesson when I stepped aboard a busy British Airways flight to Milan. I had word of a nifty little deal I could get in on, importing some cheapo but ace quality tablewear which I knew I could get knocked out down East Street Market any Sunday morning and still have time for a hot sassparella and some jellied eels.

I had to move fast so there wasn't time to take the ferry and drive. I'd had to beg, borrow and steal the money for the air ticket – I almost asked if I could have a discount if I was willing to take the seat next to the outside bog.

As everyone pushed and jostled, I managed to find my allocated seat and sank into it, ready to sleep all the way to Italy, when a harassed looking American bird approached and said wearily : "I'm sorry Sir, but I think you are in my seat."

I checked my ticket. No, I was in the right place. She showed me her ticket and, yes, it had the same seat number.

Now, of course it's the natural reaction in such trying circumstances to adopt the time-honoured policy of "first come, first serve, so fuck off", especially if it is working in your favour. But I could see from the strained look on the woman's face that she was at the point of both mental despair and physical collapse.

She told me she had been travelling all day, had suffered messed-up connections and was exhausted, so, the gentleman that I am, I insisted she take the seat while I went to look for the steward.

It wasn't good news. I was told the plane wasn't just full but was overbooked and that I'd likely be bumped off the flight, and end up being left standing on the tarmac while they headed for the wide blue yonder, but would I please stand in the galley while they tried to sort something out?

Net result? I was ushered into business-class and spent the flight in the best seat in the house, sipping Champagne. Best of all, I met up with 'Miss America' in Milan for a drink and ended up getting my leg over.

Déjà vu. A similar thing happened to me on a recent train trip to Darlington. I found the only seat left in second-class that didn't have a reserved sticker on it. Opposite sat a young couple.

A pair of businesswomen appeared claiming they had reservations. They were told (not by me): "Tough, we're already here and there's nothing on the seats to say they've been reserved."

Then another lady appeared, claiming she also had a reservation for one of this block of four seats and she was being joined down the line by a colleague who had reserved the fourth one.

The ticket collector appeared, politely trying to resolve the problem but the young couple, standing on their rights, were having none of it. In fact, they were being downright bolshie. I, meanwhile, had said I would be happy to move but would be grateful if he could find me somewhere else to sit.

Of course, he eventually laid down the law and trooped the recalcitrant duo off down the train, leaving me to gather up my belongings in my own time.

He eventually re-appeared and escorted me to a seat in first-class, commenting: "It pays to be polite. You've got your reward but I put those two arseholes in the worst seats I could find."

I don't get to travel much, unless you count the twice weekly outing to the boozer for my swift half, but when I do I believe in doing it as well as I can for as little dosh as I can get away with. I'll spend hours surfing the web trying to get the best deals and even if I've had a result and picked up a ticket for next to nothing I'll still try to improve my lot by seeing if I can then blag an upgrade. There's a definite art to the process. I don't often get to fly long-haul but flash Simon does it all the time and he's got the process down to a T.

The key, he tells me, is to dress neatly – very smart casual seems to work better than business suit because leisure travellers are usually less demanding and abrasive than business travellers and if you want favours it pays to be nice. Ask first at the ticket desk, though upgrades are usually allocated at the gate, and have some credible reason why you deserve what is, after all, a massive concession.

Shelly's Uncle Ed walks with a limp. He was offered a move from economy into business class but said his wife was with him. The stewardess offered to upgrade them both. He then told her my sister-in-law and brother-in-law were also travelling with them and, bugger me, all four got moved up to the posh seats.

Simon once bought a £350 one-way economy ticket home from Australia, asked for an upgrade and was moved into first-class for the portion from Sydney to Los Angeles where, he was told, he would have to go back into economy. In the event, he was simply asked to move back one row of seats. The regular first-class fare for the route ran into thousands but Si had paid a pittance. The fact that Simon always comes across like he could buy the airline out of his petty cash tin and the added consideration that he could charm the knickers off a nun probably has a lot to do with his impressive success rate. It also explains why he can always get a table in a restaurant which is supposedly full, or tickets to a show which sold out months ago.

Si reckons the chances of getting an upgrade, all things being equal – and remembering that some airlines never give them – is about one in eight, though he seems to do better. But though the odds are against, there's no harm in asking. After all, the worst they can do is say "no – fuck off".

Tip-time! If you should be lucky enough to be booted upstairs on a red-eye flight back from Florida or wherever, enjoy the Champagne, the Cognac, the gourmet food, the personal video player and fantasizing over the stewardess – or the steward, if that's your inclination. But, if the plane is uncrowded then when it's bye-bye's time you might be better off slipping back into cattle class and laying across a whole row of seats, raising the seat arms first, of course. For, luxurious as it might be, that plush leather seat up in first-class only reclines so far (unless it's on one of the very latest planes), and certainly isn't a bed, so don't expect a good night's kip in it.

Another tip. If you are late for your flight, never give up until you are absolutely certain that the wheels have left the ground. The fact is, there are so many flight delays in today's busy skies that you might well catch the plane even if you arrive at the airport after the flight is supposed to have taken off.

Simon reckons his record is to have arrived three-and-a-half-hours late at Heathrow yet still catch the flight he was booked on, so late was it running. Allow for the fact that Simon's a bullshitter and a congenital liar if you will, but you get my point, don't you?

On one occasion he was due to fly out to France with a group. Driving into town from his girlfriend's flat in trendy Docklands, he was held up in a massive traffic jam caused by Tower Bridge being raised.

Avoiding the outrageous car park charges at the airport – which in the short-term park can come to more than your air ticket and even in long-term are an arm-and-a-leg job – he used the ploy of parking by West Hounslow tube station and taking the tube the rest of the way into the airport (a judicious application of yellow paint in the surrounding streets has since put an end to that one).

It was 10.45 am. The flight departure time was 11 am. Taking the Underground would take too long, so Simon hailed a passing black cab: "How long to get to the airport?" he enquired.

"Oh, 15 minutes mate," came the reply.

"You've got 10," he shot back.

Despite running at Olympic finals pace, by the time he got through security, passport control and out to the gate the place was deserted.

99 per cent of people would have given up there and then but Si looked through a window and could see the tip of a tail-plane.

Looking for a way to get to it, he spotted a door marked "Private: No Admittance". It had to be the one. He turned the handle, it wasn't locked. It took him down a flight of stairs and out onto the tarmac where the ground crew where just about to wheel away the steps.

Bounding up them with Superman strides, Simon was greeted by the stewardess at the airplane door with one of the great understatements of our time: "You're cutting it a bit fine!"

Puffing and blowing, he re-gathered his composure and within seconds had, straightened his tie, pushed every strand of hair back into its immaculate place and regained his customary cool. He nonchalantly strode down the aisle, greeting his surprised travelling companions with a cheery: "Good morning everyone!" James Bond himself could not have pulled it off with more style.

Delayed flights can mean missed connections and, of course, the airlines try to absolve themselves of all responsibility. These days they are also far too often guilty of cramming a plane with passengers and ending up with more bodies than can be accommodated.

If, however, you've got all the time in the world, an overbooked flight can be the stuff of dreams.

When British Airways and British Midland introduced their shuttle flights to Glasgow, Edinburgh and Belfast, it was on the basis of no pre-booked seats, first come, first served but everyone guaranteed to get a place on the flight. The impression given was that if they had just one passenger too many then they'd simply wheel out another plane.

Of course, as anyone who knows anything about air travel will tell you, it's not quite so simple. Airlines don't have spare aircraft tucked away in some hangar at the far end of the airport, waiting for the call of duty and, even if they did, they wouldn't be able to get a slot from air traffic control to allow the extra plane to take off.

What actually happened was that they'd send a member of staff to walk around among the passengers, take a likely looking soul (usually a scruff-bag back-packer) to one side and offer them a cash incentive to miss the flight and take the next one instead.

It's a policy used by all airlines in over-booking situations. My aunt was once offered overnight accommodation in a five-star Manhattan hotel plus a flight home the next day on Concorde if she'd give up her seat on a grossly overbooked 747. Sadly she couldn't take the later flight because if she'd turned up a day late her old man, a jealous, possessive old git, would have gone ballistic.

My pal Tom is another aspiring jet-setter. His job as a production manager with a print company is pretty crappy, but it does involve a bit of travel. His most disastrous experience was on a flight back from a trade fair in the Indonesian capital of Djakarta which his boss had sent him to, all expenses paid, the lucky bastard. It was at the time of the forest fires which swept Sumatra and other islands, leaving a thick cloud of choking smoke over a wide region of South East Asia, with one of its more tragic results being the crash of an Air Garuda plane, with massive loss of life.

It did not help that the plane Tom was due to fly out on was the same service, the very next day. Lack of communication was the biggest problem. The flight was cancelled but nobody could say why or could offer advice on when the next one would be available.

Eventually, at 11.30 pm, the passengers were transferred to a hotel, only to be told they would have to pay for their own food and that, in any case, the restaurant was shut.

Delay followed delay. Airline staff just shrugged and walked away when anyone tried to ask what was going on – and nobody dared go off-airport in case something did happen.

It was great material for a novel. A diabetic's insulin had already been loaded onto the delayed plane, an epileptic also needed medication, a blind girl travelling alone was in total confusion, a woman who had a baby had time to have another one, and a young man due to be in the Jordanian capital city of Amman – the scheduled re-fuelling point – for his imminent wedding was becoming demented.

Tom had befriended an elderly Indonesian gentleman who had worked for the BBC World Service in London for years and was returning home after visiting relatives following a recent liver transplant operation. First carrying just his new friend's luggage, the task soon widened to virtually carrying the increasingly ailing man himself.

After 20 hours with no food and drink, cold, stale, inedible burgers were presented to the passengers who were by now on the point of open revolt, especially after having been loaded on a plane then offloaded again with the information that it had engine-failure. Indeed, one Aussie girl eventually lost it, went berserk and only re-gathered her senses with the arrival of fully-equipped riot police – clubs, shields, crash helmets and all.

By now, the UK media was on the case, a local newspaper reporter having phoned her editor to explain why she would be late back from her holiday. A plan was hatched for the passengers to refuse to de-plane at Gatwick and stage a sit-in to protest at the way they'd been treated.

In the event, on reaching England, some 20 flying hours later, everyone had calmed down and all they wanted to do was to get home.

This tale highlights perhaps the most frustrating facet of any complaint: not knowing what's going on or how long you will have to wait to get it sorted.

London Transport did themselves and the travelling public a truly massive favour when they introduced electronic indicator boards to let you know how long the wait for the next tube train will be. Five minutes, 10, 20 – you can usually cope, just as long as you know.

I suppose it's in the nature of transport to be chaotic and

rather inefficient but it would certainly help a lot if the operators – who have stopped calling us 'passengers' and now address us as 'customers', the silly bastards – started to act as if that really is the case.

It might be a tad unfair but personally I'm not surprised that the world's airlines have earned themselves such pungent acronyms as: 'Such A Bloody Experience Never Again' (Sabena); 'Bloody Awful' British Airways); 'Take Another Plane' (TAP Portuguese Airlines) and 'Queens And Nymphomaniacs Trained As Stewards' (Qantas).

ONE UP ON THE CLAMPERS

Of course, it's not just the jet-setters among us who have problems whenever they try to get about. My pal Dennis was in the midst of one of his frequent dabbles in the building industry and had a big refurbishment job going on in Central London. Every day he had to travel in his van to the heart of the West End and just about every day he got one or two parking tickets or a clamping. On two occasions he got both.

It was a constant war every day with this same miserable lanky long streak of piss of a parking warden. Boy did this sad git hate society; he sure had an axe to grind and took it out on every motorist he could. He was the sort who'd slap a ticket on you while you were waiting for the lights to change to green.

This right tosser was totally unapproachable and would not stand for any of it. Didn't matter if your nan was dying, if you were having an epileptic fit or the air raid sirens were about to signal World War Three – "You can't park there, mate!"

Every day, Dennis was having races with him to try to prevent the van being ticketed. Den soon became convinced that this miserable little excuse for a man was targeting him personally and was permanently hiding around the corner in wait, just so he could call in the clampers.

This whole episode went on for two weeks, almost becoming the scheduled street entertainment for the day, and other workmen and people from the nearby offices were all getting involved. When you boil it all down, Dennis was only trying to do his job: he needed his van on site to transport tools and materials and couldn't carry out his task without this – but this simple as the nose on your face fact just would not be understood by this leech of a traffic warden, who wouldn't even let him stop for a few seconds over the maximum loading time.

It's my belief that all parking wardens are wannabe policemen. I think they all applied at some stage of their sorry lives to be in the Metropolitan Police force but got rejected and settled for what they thought was the next best thing. For them it was a sort of empowerment they wouldn't find any other way.

It is as close as they are going to get to wearing a meaningful uniform and having a radio and being able to exert power over other people. You must have seen them driving around in marked police cars pretending to be the boys in blue. Wankers! I admit you do get the odd one who is all right and reasonable and who gives you a chance, but it it's a rare event. Most of them are right doughnuts too, with the IQ of a rusty spanner.

I haven't got anything against the job that they do – well, there does need to be discipline on the streets, otherwise it would be absolute chaos out there and we'd all end up in grid-lock. But to my mind they should concentrate on targeting the cars that are actually causing an inconvenience to other motorists or those drivers – and it has to be said there are many of them – who are totally ignorant and inconsiderate people.

You used to be able to reason with the wardens before they slapped a ticket on. And if your line of patter was plausible enough they'd let you get away with the extra minute's leeway you needed to do what you had to do. You always knew that if you parked up after 5 pm, especially on a wet and windy day, they would already have pissed off home. But since they went private, and started being paid on performance, the wardens have become right eager little ferrets and you can pick up a ticket with just a couple of minutes to go before the parking restrictions end of an evening.

They also pull some right strokes too, like ticketing you when you are parked on a private forecourt. What makes it worse is that there's no way of challenging them anymore. They only allow appeals on a couple of very specific grounds, like the car had been stolen or it's no longer yours. And you don't even get the chance to go to court if you want to dispute the ticket because the whole process of ticketing, fine and enforcement is automatic and they are all too quick to send the bailiffs round if you don't pay up pronto.

Anyway, every time Dennis was landed with a parking ticket it was £60 down the tubes (reduced to 30 smackers if he settled it within 28 days of issue). Whenever he got a clamp it was £105 plus a parking ticket of £60 plus four hours of pure grief – firstly getting the money, then going to the location of the council's clamping office to pay the money and then waiting hours for the men to come and remove the clamp. And I can assure you that they don't remove them as quickly as they put them on. It don't make sense really: they clamp you, supposedly, for causing an obstruction then, by clamping you, they make sure your car stays in the way for the rest of the day.

On the last day of his contract, Dennis was just getting the rest of his tools from the job. He returned to find that yet another clamp had been applied. It was the last straw as far as he was concerned. The job he had completed had become a very costly one and he was well out of pocket, with his profit for the work long since wiped out because of all those parking fines..

He knew exactly what was involved, in both time and money, to have this latest clamp removed, so he thought he would remove it himself – with a little help from another builder who was working in the area.

He let his tyre down and, with a lot of jiggling, managed to remove the clamp without causing any damage to it. He told me it was really funny how other blokes offered to assist. One guy came over with an angle grinder offering to saw the clamp off but Dennis knew that such action could well lead to further trouble and a possible charge of criminal damage if he got caught doing it.

After successfully removing the clamp, he then decided to hang it up on the railings alongside where the van had been parked. He then left a little note attached to it. It read simply: "To the clampers: YOU ARE BAD! BUT I'M BADDER!!! Have a nice day!". At that, he drove off into the sunset – nice one Dennis boy! But, please don't try this at home.

Of course, there is sometimes a human face to the establishment. A lady friend of Duncan's serves as a magistrate – yes, one of those people who sometimes make such seemingly irrational decisions and too often wear their inbred prejudices right there on their arm in full display.

Joy is, though, somewhat to the left of Labour and, even more importantly, is an understanding soul who acknowledges that the long arm of the law can be covered in warts and blemishes. Well, it seems she was sitting one day with another magistrate, a sixtyish middle-class professional woman, one of the blue-rinse brigade, who is notorious as a 'hanging judge' – a prudish, rather bigoted lady who has an avowed dislike of Asians, blacks, gays, single mothers, council house tenants and 'the lower classes'.

Appearing before them on this occasion was a young black lad of about 22, dressed in expensive Armani, wearing dark glasses, mobile phone in hand and with, doubtless, a smart BMW 3 Series parked outside, probably on a double yellow line – in short, just the sort that the old bat would usually want to throw the book at.

He had been charged with assaulting a parking warden. If found guilty he might even have gone to prison.

The warden was on hand to give evidence, along with one of his colleagues. Nasty, arrogant, spiteful – and those were just these two weasels' better traits – this sad pair trotted out a story which was obviously well rehearsed as they gave accounts which were virtually word for word the same.

Now, the accused confessed that, once the warden had well and truly wound him up, he did use his mobile phone to keep tipping the peak of the warden's cap in order to annoy him. Technically, this is, of course, assault.

The magistrates retired to consider their verdict. But instead of getting her black cap out, the old bat, to Joy's immense surprise but great delight, said: "Even if I'd been there and knew he'd hit the warden I'd have to find him not guilty. I just couldn't give those two little Hitlers the satisfaction of winning!"

Joy and the third magistrate, a rather level-headed gentleman with a trade union background and a keen sense of fair play, were in full agreement.

You can imagine the look of sheer hatred the magistrates received from the wardens when the verdict was announced. The black lad, on the other hand, was so shocked and delighted to have been let off that he vaulted over the benches and ran up to the two lady magistrates to plant big thankyou kisses on their cheeks! Everyone was falling about laughing.

"TODAY, CENTRAL LONDON——
TOMORROW VE INVADE POLAND!"

HANGING AROUND AT NUMBER 10

After failing miserably as a driving instructor due to circumstances completely beyond my control – for example, buying new cars that cost more than I could afford but let me constantly down and being harassed by the boys in blue with constant embarrassing mid-lesson pulls – I decided it was time to settle down and try to take a more sensible approach in the quest for earning a decent regular income in return for as little effort as possible, so I took myself off to college and studied electrical engineering NVQ 2.

I then landed myself a really good number as a photocopy engineer with one of the world's leading companies. I was a very small cog in an extremely large wheel, maybe, but it was a right cushy number without the need to pile on the hours I'd been working when I was teaching the world's premier collection of idiots how to steer round a busy Camberwell junction without fucking up the gearbox. Not only did the job come with an attractive salary, with paid holidays and sick pay too, but I got a nice brand-new company car which, if it went wrong, would be someone else's problem. Indeed, when the engine came off its mountings and popped the bonnet as I went over a road hump, the end result was Vauxhall recalling thousands of cars of that model so they could be strengthened – and all the while my car and all the others were off the road, I was enjoying an upgrade to a top-of-the-range Omega, leather seats, air-con and all. Add in health insurance, and an attractive bonus scheme if I met my targets and you can see how I felt I'd arrived on easy street.

There was the added advantage that, instead of being stuck in some poxy office, I was out and about all day – which gave me plenty of opportunity to do a bit of my usual ducking and diving and explained why the car's boot was often jam-packed with so many job lots of car security systems, Christmas toys, computer games or how's your father, that there was precious little room for my tools of trade and all those photocopier spare parts I was supposed to carry.

I was working for the company for about two years and was doing so well that I had been promoted three times within this period. I ended up being what they called 'the regional product specialist' for the South East.

In short time I was doing so well that I was even able to get a mortgage and for the first time buy a home of my own. I was no longer a council tenant and I reckon they must have held a firework display and Champagne party down at the town hall that night because I was at last out of their hair once and for all. Well, at least that's what we all thought at the time.

I was also able to provide properly for my kids and give them the things that they needed, like nice clothes and trips to the seaside, and still have a little left over for my own enjoyment.

One fine morning – well, actually, it was pissing down, but who cares? – I grabbed the morning post on the way out the door, so I could scan through it all whilst stuck in the morning rush hour traffic. I noticed one letter that stood out from all the rest. It was in a little brown envelope with a red stamp mark on the righthand side that read CSA.

The letter was from the Child Support Agency and demanded a reply within 14 days, which had to contain a full assessment of my current financial circumstances. There was also a comment that read to the effect that: "failure to supply this information will lead to prosecution."

The depth of information that was required was unbelievable. They wanted to know the ins-and-outs of a cat's arsehole. I had no choice but to give them what they wanted. The whole thing put the wind right up me, so I went to the local library and advice centres getting as much information as I could, as this was one subject I knew sweet f.a about. There was not that much available, and even Duncan wasn't much help, as it was a new law that had just been enforced and not even the CSA case officers themselves knew all the fine-print details.

Every time I phoned them I would get the same pat answers, which sounded like they were being read from a hymn sheet, and was advised that they had strict guidelines which they had to adhere to, with no flexibility allowed.

The assessments had to be carried out following a cast-in-stone format and with no flexibility for individual circumstances or consideration of whether or not you were already facing up to your responsibilities as an absent father. My assessment was completed within three weeks and the outcome was a demand for a wacking £500 per month that I clearly could not afford. I went through all the appeals procedures and re-assessments but the bastards just would not budge.

When I was given my pay slip the following month, it carried the message: "Re: Attachment of Earnings Order – £500" which amount had been deducted from what the company paid into my bank account. This was exactly half my dosh, meaning I had just 500 notes, just a sodding monkey, left to live on. Somehow I had to pay my mortgage, which was three-and-a-half of it on its own, cover the gas and electric bills, pay my council tax, feed and clothe myself and meet my day-to-day out-of-pocket expenses and put up with the constant direct pleas for money from my two ex-wives. And what hurt was that I knew the money the CSA mob were filching out of my pay packet was not even going directly to my kids but was being used to offset whatever handouts my exes were getting from the government.

Without my knowing exactly what was going on, the CSA had applied to the court for an attachment order on my earnings and went direct to the company I was working for to extract the money – and there was nothing I could do about it.

It didn't help that I was mainly working in Central London and had to pump the ever hungry parking meters full with absurd parking charges of £3 or more an hour out of my own pocket and then wait to claim the dosh back the following month from my employers. Nor did it help that Maggie and Shelly, since they didn't see any of the money going direct from me to them, reckoned I was now ducking out of providing support.

Needless to say, the pressures of all this were enormous. I knew I would sink rapidly and I did. The stress was unbearable, what with all the ear-wigging from the two former Mrs Rogers and the demands from the CSA. I found myself developing an awkward nervous tick, running panic attacks and generally losing grip. I went and saw a solicitor, the local citizens' advice centre and finally a money management councillor, and even booked some sessions with a psychiatrist, but none of them could offer any help beyond tea and biscuits and expressions of sympathy as I began sinking into the quicksands of debt.

The bills and resultant final demands were mounting up, until I had more bits of red paper than the Communist Party and I could see things rapidly going from bad to worse.

There was no real incentive to go to work anymore. I had no problem with the wholly reasonable idea of absent fathers being made to take responsibility for financially supporting their children but resented that my money was not going direct to them, so the mums could see I was doing my best, but were vanishing instead into some government pot buried somewhere deep in the Treasury.

It was all a vicious circle. My exes had no incentive to go out to work because that would mean them losing the state benefits they were being paid, so they wouldn't really be any better off once they had paid for child minders, fares to work and the like. What they couldn't seem to get to grips with though was that, through the CSA, the government was reclaiming from me most if not all the state pay-outs, leaving me with nothing left from which to make direct payments to my two families. Indeed, I was left with so little in the pot that it became difficult to visit the kids as often as I wanted, which only served to heighten the false impression that I had lost interest and didn't want to help with the children's upbringing.

Before, I'd been able to go out and choose coats, shoes or toys for them, I'd bought them bikes and had taken them on outings but now, though I was the ultimate source of their funding, I had no input into how it was spent nor did I get credited with having provided the money in the first place.

I was going around in circles and out of my mind with worry as my whole life changed rapidly for the worse within a few short months. I just didn't know what to do and felt like my hands were tied together. I was wearing lead boots and I was being asked to wade across an ever deepening pool of shit with the tide running against me. One day, after spending another frustrating session on the phone argy barging with the CSA and getting absolutely nowhere, I decided drastic action was needed.

Early that evening, I borrowed a couple of quid for some petrol, jumped in my car, drove up to Soho, and breezed into the first sex shop I could find. The shop assistant was a right punk-rocker type, with orange hair and was dressed in black fishnets and leather bondage gear. She had rings in her eyebrows and nose and who knows where else that I couldn't see, despite the skimpy nature of her leather skirt.

I asked her where in the shop I could find a good strong set of metal handcuffs but I had a very different purpose in mind to that which she usually sold them for.

After making my purchase – which was discretely wrapped in brown paper, of course – I made my way to Downing Street, that most famous address in London. I parked my car up the side of Whitehall, and locked the vehicle up, leaving the keys to the cuffs inside the glove box. I walked the short distance to the gates which now block Downing Street off from the general public. Here two police officers were on duty, screening visitors. I asked one of them if I could deliver a letter of protest about the CSA and its activities to the prime minister at Number 10, but I was blankly refused entry.

We then got into a rather heated political debate about the CSA and their methods but the copper really didn't give a shit as he was due to go off duty within about 20 minutes of me getting there and was more interested in what his missus had prepared for his tea than in any problems I might have. In any event, he didn't make the laws but, come hell or high water, he believed they should be applied to the letter. So I knew deep down I was not going to get anywhere with him or with my letter – but I felt so strongly about needing to make my point to someone in authority that I decided a man has to do what a man has to do.

It was then I produced my pre-prepared handcuffs. One part was already attached to my left wrist, which I had been keeping buried in my pocket all the time. In an instant, I snapped the other part onto the gates. You should have seen that copper's face drop when he realised I'd done a suffragette impersonation and was now firmly affixed to the ironwork. He just couldn't believe I'd done something so drastic.

His reaction was right to the point: "What the fuck did you do that for, you little tosser," he yelled at me. He immediately got on his two-way radio and, credit where it's due, the response was breathtakingly rapid. Police cars arrived from all directions, with blue lights flashing and sirens wailing, and within minutes Whitehall was white-taped off and closed to all traffic. The coppers who attended were men whose prime job was protecting diplomats and key politicians. They drove flash red police cars and, so I'm told, they are always armed. Well, nobody shot me, but I got a right ear full of verbal abuse off them as they were really pissed off with me and my antics. A couple of them were right nasty pieces of work too. They really thought they were the bees-knees, a cut above everyone else, and they obviously thought a little toe-rag like me was akin to something nasty they'd just trod in.

I was obviously classed as a security risk too, bearing mind where I was, and as a result I was searched so thoroughly I thought maybe they had a crush on me. Ten minutes later, another police van arrived and the driver, a right big bleeder, with biceps like tree trunks, produced a very large pair of bolt croppers but they weren't sharp enough to cut through the strengthened steel of the cuffs. Shit, did he curse as he tried to snap through the metal, using words a sheltered little soul like me has rarely heard before.

I started to get a bit worried because he was really beginning to lose his rag and looked like he might start using the bolt cutters directly on me. The silly sod never thought of cutting the chain that linked the handcuffs together but instead kept trying to get through the part that went around my wrist. He kept hissing, "Now jack it in you arsehole – where's the keys?" but I wasn't about to tell him, now was I?

Giving it up as a bad job, he then got onto his oppo to call the fire brigade out and those lads arrived mob handed, which made an even bigger farce of the whole thing. Of course, those lads did the job in a jiffy, leaving the Old Bill looking rather stupid – which made them even more miffed with me. I was then arrested.

After the police had confirmed who I was and had at last cottoned on to why I was carrying out this one-man demonstration, I was released without charge, getting off with just a severe telling-off for wasting their time.

In reality, I had achieved nothing to help me and all the other dads going through the same shit as me, though I do hear that the CSA is likely to be abandoned in favour of a more workable and fairer system which hits the defaulters rather than those like me who make a real effort to maintain parental contact and involvement with their kids. At least I had the satisfaction of blowing off a bit of steam and doing something about it, however ineffectual, rather than just sitting round moaning. I hadn't even won any publicity for the cause, making neither the Ten O'clock News or The Sun, and I'm sure the residents of Downing Street – our Tony and his crew – didn't have a clue what was going on.

Unfortunately, two months later, unable to keep pace with my ever rising mountain of debt, I was forced to give up my home and my job and ended up back on the streets again. So here I am, back to where I started, kipping on friends' sofas, ducking and diving, bobbing and weaving, still trying to survive against all the odds. I've got a few little deals brewing away and I've even managed to get another set of wheels – and they are taxed, MOTd and insured too. I'm still in there fighting my corner, me old son.

They say life begins at 40. That may be so, but there's a pretty long and rough apprenticeship before you get to that promised golden age. So, I'll just keep on plugging away and you know one thing's for sure: if anyone tries to put one over on me, well, as I'm certain you don't need telling, I ain't 'aving that!

FOOTNOTES

USING THE SMALL CLAIMS COURT

Contact your local county court and ask them to send you a claims form. This will need to be completed with all the information relating to the claim, including all the details of whom you are claiming against. and what it is for.

The court will make a charge. The cost will depend on how much you are claiming and whether you wish the matter to be dealt with in the Small Claims Court, which is essentially an arbitration set-up, or in full court.

If you win your case such court fees can be recovered from the other side. The people you are claiming against will be called the 'Defendant' and you will be called the 'Claimant' or the 'Plaintiff'.

Any civil action relating to money only and where the value is under £5,000 can be dealt with by the small claims court. Anything over that amount or relating to goods or disputes over credit agreements will be dealt with in the County Court.

When making a claim you will also need to attach to your completed claim form a document called a 'Particular of Claims'. This must include certain specific information. It is like a record of events and includes times and dates and important information relating to your claim. It can also include any other information which you feel to be important.

At the end of the document you state exactly what you are claiming. The final part is a declaration reading: "I believe that the facts stated in these particulars of claim are true". This should then be dated and signed by you. The particulars of claim should also include an address at which you can receive documents.

If you intend to produce documentary evidence to support your claim – say, an invoice, receipt or letter – copies of any such items must be sent to the other party at least 14 days before the hearing date (it is only fair that both sides should have forewarning of any written evidence which is to be produced). It is sensible to send these by recorded delivery post.

Once all the above is completed the form should be sent to the court. A summons will then be served on the defendant by post. Any defence must be filed within 14 days of receiving the summons.

In due course, the court will advise both sides of the allotted hearing date which will usually be within a three-month period.

If the defendant still has not filed a defence by the date of the hearing, the district judge will then decide the case there and then or can set up a timetable for how the case will continue. If a defence has been filed, the hearing will go ahead and both sides will be given the opportunity to state their case.

If the small claims procedure is used, the hearing will be in front of an arbitrator in the fairly informal setting of a private room, rather than in the rather forbidding setting of open court.

One advantage of using the small claims procedure is that whether you win or lose you are only responsible for your own legal costs (with the exception of court fees, which can be recovered by the winning side from the loser) and, indeed, there is every encouragement to handle the case for yourself rather than being represented by a solicitor. If you are not legally represented, one of the arbitrator's duties is to argue any points of law with the other side on your behalf.

If you are in receipt of social security benefits or are on a low income, you may be able to receive free legal advice under the so-called Green Form Scheme.

WHAT IF THE OTHER BASTARD'S NOT INSURED?

Ok, so the accident is not your fault but what happens if you try to claim against the other party only to find out that they are not insured?

Under pressure from the government of the day, some decades ago the insurance companies came together to set up the MIB (or Motor Insurance Bureau) into which each of them contributes a portion of their premium revenue. These monies are then used to help recompense anyone who is unfortunate enough to be the victim of an accident with an uninsured motorist.

My car was once smashed up the back at a red traffic light by a car whose driver then gave me false information. I suffered whiplash injuries and wanted to claim for these plus the damage to my car but after I'd sent my insurance company the details which the other driver had furnished they wrote back to say the information was false and told me he was untraceable.

The advice was to make a claim with the MIB – but don't think for one minute that this is an easy process, because it isn't! It took exactly two years before the claim was settled.

First they get the police to supply a full copy of the accident report and confirm that the driver cannot be traced and then they undertake their own enquiries, which take several months.

After this had been done in my case, I was contacted by a private investigator who had been instructed by the MIB to interview me at my home and who took another full statement. It took three full months for that report to make its way back to the MIB – I haven't a clue why it took so long; all part of the red tape treatment, I suppose, unless it had taken her all that time to crawl home round the M25, of course.

Next the MIB contacted the DSS Compensation Recovery Unit to see if I had been receiving any state benefits as a result of my injuries. If I had, then the amount that the DSS had paid to me would be deducted from the offer made by the MIB and returned to the DSS. Such a check is usually made in the early stages of the claim and then repeated before the agreed payment for the claim is actually made to you.

You should be aware that the insurance companies now pool information on a centralised computer database. This contains information on who has made claims, what for, and what amount was paid out.

This means that anyone filling in a form with false or incomplete information – whether it be a proposal form or a claim form – will most likely be found out, not only meaning that any subsequent claim will be thrown out but also rendering such a person liable to possible prosecution for making a false declaration.

Lots of people are confused by the term 'knock for knock'. What it means, in essence, is that instead of arguing over who is to blame and then trying to get money out of each other, the insurance companies operate an agreement under which each pays its own insured's claim whether they were to blame for the accident or not – on the principal that, with thousands of claims occurring each year, it will be a case of swings and roundabouts.

Such an arrangement saves the cost of lengthy negotiations and thus is said to help keep insurance premiums down (or, cynics prefer to believe, helps boost insurance company profits).

The worry is that, with your own company having paid out your claim you will then unfairly lose your no-claims bonus. The insurance companies insist that this will not be the case and that you will only lose your bonus if they come to the conclusion that the accident was your fault – but the decision rests with them, and many motorists believe themselves to have been wrongly held to blame, though, of course, that doesn't always mean they were indeed the innocent party as few people like to admit they are crap drivers. I was once shown a claim form on which the policyholder answered "No" to the question "Were you to blame for the accident?". It turned out he had been driving the wrong way down a dual carriageway at the time. Asked why he didn't consider himself to blame, he responded with sincerity: "Because the other driver wasn't looking where he was going"!

Controversy also surrounds the so-called protected no-claims bonus. It usually takes three or four years without a claim before you qualify for a full no-claims bonus (which is usually 65 per cent). Obviously, this is a big discount which you do not want to jeopardise.

At this point, most companies will offer a protected no-claims bonus scheme which means that, for an additional annual premium, you will be allowed to make up to two claims within one year without losing any of your bonus. Knowing that you have a good driving record with them to date, the insurance company is thus earning itself some extra premium with relatively little risk attached and, as I'm sure we all appreciate, they'll squeeze every financial advantage they can.

Given that many policies also make you pay the first part of any claim (perhaps £50 or even as high as £250) the no-claims bonus is a major disincentive for claiming for anything short of a major prang. Add together the excess and the bonus you will lose on renewal and you might find the company will actually be clawing back more than they have to paid out to you for the claim! In essence, it means that for any claim of less than £200-£300 you will be financially better off swallowing the loss yourself – which rather negates the whole point of having insurance in the first place.

One last piece of advice on car insurance. If you are

phoning round for quotes and they take down all your details and offer a monthly installment plan for the premiums, there's a chance they might make a credit check on you without telling you that's what they are doing.

You should make sure they do no such thing until you have actually decided that they are the company you will be going with. Remember, credit searches show up on your record and too many of them being made might lead someone else to turn you down for credit on, say, that new washing machine or video player you've got your eye on.

Operating in a similar way to the MIB, the Criminal Injuries Compensation Board was set up by the government in order to provide some financial support for people unlucky enough to be injured as a result of other people's criminal acts.

If, for example, you have been assaulted and the attacker has not been found by the police after a full investigation then you can make a claim to the CICB.

You will be sent an application form, which is quite detailed, and may be required to provide certain documentation before your claim is considered.

The amount they decide to offer you will depend on the seriousness of your injuries and when receiving your claim form you will also be supplied with a chart which indicates approximately how much compensation is paid for certain injuries.

IN YOUR OWN INTERESTS

Impulse buying is a powerful thing, sometimes leading us to rush into purchases which we might regret later on. That's not too much of a problem if the item concerned is some loud shirt which you will end up giving to Oxfam, or a cheapo CD which sounds like it was recorded in someone's bathroom, but it could be the cause of long-term regret if it's a new car, motor caravan or fully-fitted kitchen that you are laying out for.

In the urge of excitement to buy what's caught your eye, it's all too easy to get carried away. I'm sure it's something that happens to us all from time to time.

Besides considering whether it really is something you (a) want (b) need and (c) can afford, it's also worth spending a bit of time looking for how best to buy it.

Can you find it easily and more cheaply elsewhere? In the case of something like a car, will there be proper back-up service? How are you going to fund the purchase?

Remember that with cars all showroom prices are negotiable – whether the vehicle is new or secondhand – and, what's more (though few people appreciate it) so is the interest rate you will be charged on any loan you take out for the purchase.

My experience has been that, in order to secure the business, the salesman or the finance company can be negotiated down in what they are asking and that's can sometimes be by as much as half the interest rate first quoted!

It's worth a try. At worst, they will just say "no", at best you'll be saving some sovs.

Never be afraid to try for a deal, even if such negotiations don't come easily (it's amazing how embarrassed many people get when it comes down to discussing money), which reminds me of the young lad who walked into the Virgin megastore and came out with two packets of Mates because he was too embarrassed to ask for a copy of "Des O'Connor's Greatest Hits".

TAKE CREDIT

Any time you sign on the dotted line of a credit card application or agreement form you are authorising the company concerned to carry out a search to see if you are credit worthy.

Banks, finance companies and other lenders use credit agencies to check people out. Such agencies hold files which contain information about you supplied from across the credit industry. From this data they can establish your credit profile and using this they will decide whether or not to provide the funding or facilities which you require (such as an overdraft or a line of credit).

Your credit file will reveal if you are registered on the electoral register at the address you have given and will state how long you have been there. It will also reveal anybody else who is registered at the same address (though this is no longer allowed to affect your credit rating).

The search will uncover a record of any other outstanding finance or credit agreements you have with anybody else, so it is important that on any application form you complete you tell the truth. If the prospective lender sees something you have not declared then they are likely to refuse you credit.

Your credit file will also include details of how reliable a payment record you have on previous and current credit agreements. Did you make your hire purchase or credit card payments on time? Did you ever fail to pay altogether? Did you ever have to make an agreement to pay your outstanding balance on revised terms? Did you ever have a county court debt judgement registered against you? Have you been bankrupt? Such details are kept on file for six years after the expiry of the credit agreement concerned or the conclusion of any court proceedings.

It is on the basis of this past record that your current credit rating is based. What this rating does is assess the risk which might be involved in making you a loan.

Obviously, the credit companies have a duty to their shareholders and also to their other borrowers and, indeed, to you yourself, to make sure that you are not overstepping your ability to pay. They want to ensure that they do not advance you loan on which you are likely to default.

This is where you need to be careful. Sometimes we apply on impulse for credit to buy things that have taken our fancy or complete an application for a credit card just for the sake of it. You should be aware that, as I've already pointed out, every time you do this a search is registered on your file and a note of this will remain there for two years – so make sure you really want to go through with it before you allow them to institute a search.

Too many searches in a small amount of time doesn't look good on your record – it looks like you have been chasing around after credit and might be overstretching yourself.

It might be that all these searches have merely occurred because you have been shopping around a bit, trying to get the best deal on a personal loan, a home improvement loan, car hire-purchase or a credit card. In fact, though, you can get all the information you want on the fine details of the deal from these companies before you go ahead with a formal credit application – so don't make one unless you definitely want to go through with it.

Now here comes the bad news of all this. If you have got a finance agreement and haven't maintained it properly or, indeed, not paid it at all, you are going to find it difficult to get further credit.

If you have made late payments occasionally then you will have built a slightly dodgy profile as it will seem you are already fully stretched – a factor which will make you look a bit of a risk to the company considering your latest application.

If you have got into serious arrears and have stopped making repayments altogether then it is most likely that a default notice will have been attached to your file and you will almost certainly be turned down for future loans, at least by respectable companies, though you might be able to raise funding at exorbitant rates from companies who portray themselves as the friends of people with poor credit ratings but which are, in fact, little short of loan sharks. Getting in their grips really is the road to misery and ruin and even if you file for personal bankruptcy, those evil people will not let you off the hook.

Before taking out any loan make sure you have shopped around for the best deal and checked out all the implications of the contract which you are about to enter into. Credit is a very serious matter. Find someone – possibly a friend who works in a bank or a family member who has already been through all the trauma of credit problems – who can give you proper advice on what you are getting into. If you have a professional financial advisor ask them. Most importantly, if in doubt, leave alone!

Be very cautious if you are asked to be a guarantor for someone else's credit agreement – even if that person is your best friend or a close relative.

Now what if your credit application is turned down? The lender is under no obligation to tell you why. That might sound a little unfair but, think about it, if a friend asks you to lend them a tenner, do you think you should be obliged to tell them the real reason why you are saying no (i.e: because you feel you will never get it back!)?

You do, though, have the right of seeing your personal credit file on which they have based their decision (they must by law give you the name and contact details of the credit search company they have used and if any of the details are wrong or out of date you have a legal right to insist on your credit record being corrected though the credit search company can only do this on the instruction of the company which filed the information with them).

It may be, for instance, that another member of your family (perhaps your father or your son) has the same initials and that details of their bad credit have been mistakenly attached to your file.

MARTIN ROGERS'
10 GOLDEN RULES OF
SUCCESSFUL COMPLAINING

1. Find something to complain about!: Well, you have to start somewhere.

2. Get your facts right: Make sure you have everything properly detailed. Beware the temptation to exaggerate – it will backfire. If you were delayed an hour, don't claim it was three.

3. Keep full records: Make a note of every call and every letter, the name of the person you spoke to and what was said. Receipts are important – keep them safe.

4. Don't be aggressive or offensive: Measured sarcasm can work wonders but if you insult people they will become bloody minded. Try to inject a sense of humour – once you've got someone smiling or laughing the battle is half won.

5. Find allies: It's amazing how even people within the organisation you are fighting can be enlisted to provide both moral and practical support. Get them on your side and you're halfway there.

6. Know who you are up against: Anyone in business will tell you the two most important people in any company they deal with are the girl on reception, who has her pulse on what's going on and where everyone is, and the person in accounts who prepares the cheques for signature. Do a bit of investigating. You might find the person who is dealing with your

complaint shares some hobby or other interest with you – indulge in some small talk and they'll think you are a like-minded soul and become much more amenable.

7. Don't be greedy: While you are entitled to have things put right, don't try to take unfair profit from the situation. If your claim is unreasonable then it's likely to be dismissed out of hand.

8. Go legal: If things are not going the right way, don't delay too long before going to law. A solicitor's letter can work wonders, a writ even more so. You should not let the fear of massive legal costs deter you – use the small claims court and everything can be kept within affordable proportions.

9. Don't lose your sense of humour: Life is but a game! If you don't take it all too seriously, complaining can be a lot of fun. Remember too, by not taking their crap you are helping everyone else to get a fair deal in the future.

10. Don't give up: Never forget my time-honoured maxim: "I ain't 'aving that!".

VOTE FOR ME,
I'LL SET YOU FREE!

So it came down to a toss-up between Tory Blair and Vague Hague – now where's the choice in that?

Never mind, next time round there will be a real option, with Martin Rogers standing for the I Ain't 'Aving That Party under the following manifesto:

- Three old laws to be removed from the statute book for each new one enacted.
- Free kebabs for all after 2 am.
- Taxis and buses to be banned from bus lanes.
- All sleeping policemen to be woken up and told to 'piss off!'
- Y-fronts to be made a criminal offence.
- All foxes to be issued with red coats and riding crops so they can go people hunting.
- London black cab drivers to be forced to go 'south of the river'.
- Every driver who is clamped to get a £20 Marks & Spencer voucher.
- Complaints against the police to be investigated by members of the public and not the police themselves.
- Anyone with a pothole in their street to be exempted from road tax.
- All old age pensioners to receive £500 a week and a free ticket to Royal Ascot.
- Windsor Castle to be changed into social housing.
- All fake Cockney celebrities to be taught Queen's English under duress.

Remember: Martin Rogers is us! – see you at the polling booth next time around.

Are you having problems with the system? Don't let 'em grind you down: let us know what's going on and share your story with the rest of us. Martin Rogers and his team are waiting to help, 'cause, as you know, "we ain't 'aving that".

Visit us today at:
www.iaintavingthat.com
or e-mail: martinrogers@iaintavingthat.com